TALES OF SPLENDANIA

A GOLDEN WISH

T.O. GRIFFITHS

Cover Designed by T.O. GRIFFITHS.

Published by T.O. GRIFFITHS.

ISBN: 978-1-7397337-0-4 (Paperback)

ISBN: 978-1-7397337-1-1 (eBook)

ISBN: 978-1-7397337-2-8 (Hardcover)

DEDICATION

To Becky,

Your bedtime story has become my dream come true.

T.O. GRIFFITHS

CONTENTS

~ Chapter 1 ~ Welcome to Splendania 1

~ Chapter 2 ~ Glimmers of Gold 13

~ Chapter 3 ~ The Spellbound Woods.................. 27

~ Chapter 4 ~ Dangers from the Deep 45

~ Chapter 5 ~ The Courage of Brothers............... 54

~ Chapter 6 ~ Beware the Golden Wish 66

~ Chapter 7 ~ Revelations.................................... 76

~ Chapter 8 ~ The Golden One............................. 88

~ Chapter 9 ~ Of Witches & Dragons 94

Epilogue 106

About The Author 110

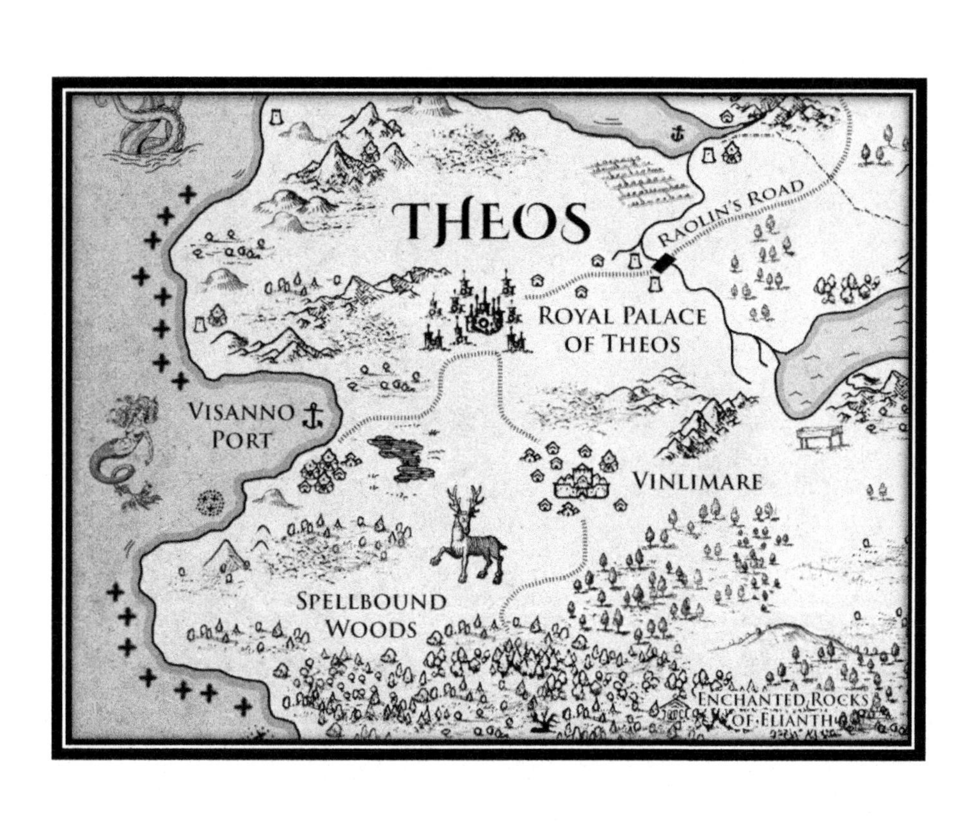
THEOS
Raolin's Road
Royal Palace
of Theos
Visanno
Port
Vinlimare
Spellbound
Woods
Enchanted Rocks
of Elianth

~ CHAPTER 1 ~

WELCOME TO SPLENDANIA

Long ago in an ancient land, full of wondrously wild, sometimes terrifying, and often beautiful magical creatures, there lived the proud people of Splendania.

Three realms made up the Kingdom of Splendania, and the largest of the three was Theos — a green and luscious land, where the towering Royal Palace stood beautifully high and majestic amongst the clouds and shone as a beacon of white and gold to all the people in Splendania.

This marvellous land of whimsical waterfalls, enchanted forests and hidden creeks was the envy of the other realms, for it was calm, most of the time, and without marauding magical monsters. Of course, there was the occasional disappearance of wanderers in the Spellbound Woods, captured by the mysterious Grey Goblins, but for the most part, it was a place of wonderful variety and astonishment.

There were enchanting creatures like the Dart Hares that could climb trees with extraordinary agility and could pounce between the branches at breakneck speed; it was indeed a true sight to behold.

There were Silverprong Stags, whose antlers were streaked with silver that grazed peacefully in the vast forests, and for the lucky few who would see them at night, the Bright Tails, whose beautiful tails of hundreds of feathers would illuminate in the darkness with vivid blues and greens.

It was unknown how many species of hidden, glorious creatures roamed the lands and skies of Splendania, but each realm had its own unique and fascinating creatures that were all hunted and fought regularly by the people of Splendania.

Far away, over beautiful valleys, dense and unexplored forests, sweeping hills and broad, treacherous rivers were the Frozen Wastes of Ovamthia. This was a cold, desolate place where the fiercest creatures of all Splendania roamed.

High atop the mountain peaks lived the petrifying

Ice Dragons and the blood-curdling Snow Trolls that were known to take children from the small, scattered colonies, and take them high up the perilous, snowy mountain peaks, never to be seen again.

Ovamthia was in the shadow of a colossal mountain range known and feared by all; it was named Dagger Falls, after the sharp and jagged cliffs. No Splendanian dared to venture up there, as it was the dwelling of the Ice Dragons.

The Ovamthians all lived in fear of their terrifying roars that echoed down the slopes and filled everyone with dread each night. The people of Ovamthia were cold and hardy; they were not very fond of outsiders, and they kept to themselves.

Ovamthia was ruled over by an ill-tempered and tyrannical King named Raolin the Undefeated, so named for his love for barbaric, needless duels with citizens looking to find fame by defeating him in single combat.

None had yet succeeded, but Raolin now brandished the gruesome scars of those who came close. One day perhaps, he would be challenged by a worthy contestant.

Built into the cliffs of Dagger Falls, the dark and uninviting castle of King Raolin overlooked an unsightly tournament arena. Dark history surrounded this arena, and this was where King Raolin was challenged by his citizens to the death.

Even further from Theos was the realm of Valastry, a barren desert with scorching heat and waves of dunes as far as the eye could see. This dangerous land was hard to traverse and even harder to survive within. There were hundreds of cavernous caves and deep canyons where monsters made their lairs, and the sandy surface was scattered with the remnants of ancient battles fought long ago.

Some brave Knights and adventurers had been lucky to find exceptional weapons and armour here, some of which were imbued with magical powers and once used by the perished soldiers that lay in the Wastes for all time.

Here in Valastry, there prowled vicious creatures like the Giant Sand Spiders, the terrifying Scorpix's with stingers the size of spears, and not least of all, a fire-breathing Griffin named Cloudspike that terrorised the skies above the small settlements and lived on the rocky peaks far out in the desert.

The faraway realm of Valastry was governed by a dutiful daughter of a recently deceased King and Queen, whose lives were lost while on an unsuccessful Royal Hunt for the Griffin, Cloudspike.

Her name was Veridis, and unlike her mother and father, she was cherished by the Valastrians, for she was kind, always wanted what was best for her people, and showed empathy for the hardships they all endured.

All of Splendania was obsessed with hunting the many magical creatures and monsters of the Three Realms. There were frequent, extensive Monster Hunts, as the Splendanians called them, where huge hunting parties of Theosians, Ovamthians and Valastrians - young and old - would pursue fame and fortune to hunt and kill the fiercest monsters.

Most of Splendania's inhabitants believed that hunting magical creatures gave them the animal's power, but even more important and precious than this, they were given their 'Special' for brave deeds and hunting prowess.

Some did not take part in the Monster Hunts in defiance, and they were mostly thought of as treasonous cowards, but at heart, they simply did not want to cause harm to innocent animals.

Being granted a Special during the sprawling, colourful and festive Day of the Specials was the highest honour a Splendanian could receive, as it cemented their legacy forevermore as a celebrated Monster Hunter.

The whole of Splendania was invited to the Day of the Specials every year; it was always in the summertime when the weather was hot and everyone was in high spirits to see who was awarded Specials for their brave, heroic deeds. This day was the only day there was absolute peace between each realm and its rulers.

Each of the Kings, Queens, and the High King of

Splendania put forward their champions to be awarded a Special, and the elders of Theos would judge their contestants and award them when in agreement. It was a day like no other, with brilliant entertainment, tournaments of jousting and on-stage plays that recalled the great battles of Splendania, and the most magnificent of the Royal Hunts.

The three realms of Splendania were ruled by a loud, opulent, and powerful High King, Magnus the Mighty, who had a passion for swords, axes, and all things that he deemed colossal.

The Royal Palace of Theos was known across Splendania for the uncountable weapons, armour and the King's magical creature trophies that adorned the high armoury walls. Most recently of which, the head of a hideously ugly Banshee that he trapped in a snare and beheaded with his gigantic great sword, Kingbreaker.

King Magnus the Mighty was awarded his Special, Mighty, for leading the battle of the River Dragon, Bildris, and slaying the thundering beast with his glorious golden axe with one clean, powerful blow after a long and vicious battle that almost cost him his life.

The King managed to leap onto Bildris's head from a cliff and strike down hard for the killing blow as his King's Guard watched in awe.

Many of the King's Guards had fantastical Specials

for protecting the King whilst on the very exclusive Royal Hunts, which only the bravest warriors and knights could attend.

There were large gatherings of Splendanians to wish them good fortune, and the whole realm would be in high spirits for the successful return of their King, Kingsmen and their triumph of killing a deadly monster.

However, some Splendanians were under the impression that this was a needless act of violence against creatures that did not harm anyone unless provoked, but they kept that to themselves as the consequence for speaking against the Royal Hunts was harrowing, to say the least.

His wife, who ruled by his side was the flawlessly majestic High Queen, Katarina the Paladin. Queen Katarina the Paladin was respected and revered across the three realms for her beauty, wisdom, and abundance of ancient knowledge that she sought above all else in her sprawling royal library that was filled with maps, texts that detailed battles long ago, and manuscripts containing vital information about the creatures and monsters of the three realms.

Katarina the Paladin was bestowed her Special, Paladin, after establishing unity between the leaders of the three realms, which included her husband the King.

Theos was a much sought-after land in comparison

to the other, hardy, and dangerous realms, and so, it was understandable that the rulers of Valastry and Ovamthia wanted to take the calmer, more inhabitable lands for themselves, and there were very occasional battles between the armies of the realms, which King Magnus the Mighty and the Knights of Theos repelled time and time again.

Queen Katarina the Paladin thought of a simple idea to stop this mindless warmongering, and that was to align their interests to one common goal as well as punish those who didn't abide by it — the ultimate prize to whoever claims the Golden Horn of the elusive Golden Unicorn, as well as a royal decree, a large residence with land in Theos, and a huge amount of gold, naturally.

This was a feat that had never been accomplished, and the prize was far too great to not aspire to win. Of course, Queen Katarina knew this all too well, for she was aware of only one Golden Unicorn that had scarcely been seen or traced; therefore, she knew it would be an age of peace until it was found at least.

Indeed, there was relative peace amongst the realms for many years, for the Golden Unicorn had still yet to be found and slain.

The King and Queen were not the only Royals in the magnificent Palace of Theos. Their daughter, the adventurous and dazzlingly pretty Princess Vanadae, lived there with extraordinarily blue eyes and long brown hair.

Vanadae loved nothing more than to explore and play in the palace gardens seeking unseen, hidden creatures like Pixies, Fairies and Goblins.

Vanadae had an admiration for unicorns over any other creature. Even though she had never laid eyes on one, she had heard astonishing tales of their grace and beauty.

She was also one of the few Splendanians who was under the impression that the unicorns, along with the sole Golden Unicorn, must dwell together in one place, hidden from the outside world. Owing to her curious side, she had an inkling as to where that could be, but only time would reveal her suspicions.

It was her wish that Splendanians would stop hunting unicorns and magical creatures altogether and that she would be appointed to keep them safe and protected. It was unfortunate that her mother, Queen Katarina the Paladin, had made such a prize for the Golden Unicorn's demise, but she understood that this treaty was made before she was born, and she knew why it had been made — for the greater good of Splendania.

Vanadae's opinion about unicorns was a very uncommon and dangerous one; one that she had to hide, for she could bring doubt and uncertainty to the peace that her mother had worked hard to bring about decades ago.

Vanadae had a younger brother, a shy Prince named

Galderon; tall and dark-haired, with deep green eyes. Galderon, like many young boys, wanted to please his father with all his endeavours. He was dedicated to following in King Magnus the Mighty's footsteps and hoped to lead sprawling Royal Hunts when he was old enough and to one day claim his own magical monster trophy.

This would grant him his very own Special, which he wanted most, as it would ensure the admiration of his royal subjects for all time.

Vanadae and Galderon were told striking tales as young children that still filled them with fear and wonder. They were both commanded never to venture to Ovamthia or Valastry.

'For obvious reasons,' King Magnus the Mighty would often shout at them in his usual exaggerated way.

'Not only would you face the perilous terrain and weather, but also the terrifyingly deadly monsters. You are forbidden to enter these lands until you are of age, is that understood? You have everything you could want in our perfect palace, do not seek danger needlessly!' the King would caution, rather hypocritically.

But Galderon always wondered why there had not been a brave Knight that had yet slain an Ice Dragon, and whether one day he could be the first Splendanian to accomplish this impossible task in Ovamthia.

He often drifted into daydreams of how exactly one would go about attempting to slay an Ice Dragon, or indeed if it were even possible with normal weaponry.

Vanadae was not concerned with these creatures and monsters at all. Whilst she too desired to travel to the far reaches of the realms, it was merely to learn more about them rather than slay them for a *silly little title*, as she often thought of the Specials.

Vanadae was also very keen to meet the King of Ovamthia and Veridis of Valastry, in a bid to gain their favour to allow her to freely explore the realms in the future, as well as bring peace across the Kingdom without the need to hunt the rarest, most precious creature of them all.

Deep within the Royal Library of Theos, Queen Katarina the Paladin had a vast collection of beautifully illustrated maps of Splendania, which included each realm and its most notable areas.

The largest of these maps was a towering ten feet high and equally as wide; it was indeed a true sight to see, and a ladder was needed to inspect the top edges closely.

What Galderon and Vanadae found most fantastic about these maps, was the stunningly detailed drawings of the magical monsters that could be located in specific parts of each realm.

The Ice Dragons were drawn, perched menacingly atop Dagger Falls in Ovamthia, and Galderon loved to inspect the illustration and try his best to replicate it. Vanadae, on the other hand, would often closely observe the realms and their monsters.

She was known to ask so many questions that Queen Katarina would often pretend she did not know the answers to, for she had learned the hard way that an entire day could be swallowed up by continuous questioning from her inquisitive children.

Therefore, the Queen would usher Vanadae and Galderon outside to 'play' or 'do something useful,' as Queen Katarina enjoyed her quiet time of study when she could seldom find the time.

~ CHAPTER 2 ~

GLIMMERS OF GOLD

Queen Katarina the Paladin was sitting along the shore of the palaces' divine and secretive Lake of Wishes whilst reading an ancient book detailing long-forgotten magical creatures and where they used to dwell.

Meanwhile, Princess Vanadae was playing in the stunningly beautiful and seemingly boundless Royal Rose Gardens, searching for Pixies, which she often did on a 'boring day' like today.

She had heard tales of the mysterious Lost City of Pixies but had no idea how to find it. Therefore, she thought that occasionally looking out for it was the best way forward.

King Magnus the Mighty was also pretty occupied, as he was very much enjoying himself as he led Prince Galderon around his gigantic armoury for what seemed like the thousandth time. Galderon did not mind in the slightest, as this was his favourite place to be.

He would always find a new weapon or piece of armour that he had never seen before. Fortunately, as the collection was constantly being added to from hunts, adventures and exploratory missions, there was never any hope of him seeing them all.

As the King was exhibiting his collection, he was giving a very one-sided conversation about the history of how he claimed each sword and axe.

Galderon thought it was far too much information about how he claimed each of the magical creature's trophies adorned on the walls; the recent Banshee in particular, which was the remains of a grotesque, scaled woman's head with a long protruding tongue and slimy hair.

The Prince would always follow the King quietly, in wonder, and would pay special attention to the glinting golden and silver blades of the King's most magnificent swords.

On this particular day, he was drawn to one he had not seen before — a remarkable steel sword with a golden hilt and handle, decorated with fascinating markings down the centre of the gleaming blade that seemed to flicker with vivid colours of different light as he turned it in his hand. Galderon was utterly bewitched by its beauty.

'Father, where did this sword come from?' Galderon asked in astonishment at the sword's magnificence. 'This sword is like nothing else I've ever seen!'

'Ah, Starbolt is its name, my son,' replied King Magnus the Mighty proudly. 'It is a relic from an ancient war where magic was entwined with the weapons of men. Rammir the Cunning found it in Valastry, deep within a cavern in the Barren Wastes, now a graveyard of soldiers from an ancient war.

I have found no use for it, as it's far too small for me,' King Magnus said whilst gesturing to his gigantic size.

'And alas, magic and men have seldom coincided for generations. Wouldn't it be astonishing to witness the power of magical weapons being used on a battlefield?'

Galderon said nothing but agreed and looked down upon the shining steel. He could feel something powerful resonating from the sword, so he put it back quickly, alarmed and entranced by it.

Princess Vanadae was high atop a balcony nearing the edge of the Royal Rose Garden; the view from up there was breathtaking and stretched far out across Theos.

On a cloudless day, you could almost make out the peaks of Dagger Falls, Queen Katarina would tell Vanadae, but she was always sceptical.

Vanadae, lost in the beauty of the view, suddenly heard a commotion down below. Two stable boys were murmuring and running up the Palace's steep walkways. She could hear the muffled words they were blabbering to each other in their ascent.

Surely, she had to know more! Vanadae loved to hear news from anywhere, anything or anyone. Maybe this was something to end her boredom, she hoped wildly.

The Princess leapt down in pursuit and finally caught up with them in excitement.

'Princess Vanadae, you startled us! What can we do for you, your Highness?' the taller stable boy asked, turning a slightly deeper shade of purple than he already was, as not only was talking with a Princess rather intimidating, but Vanadae's beauty also didn't help.

'I couldn't make out what you were spluttering to each other on the way up, but it sounded like you've found something?' Vanadae asked inquisitively, expecting an immediate response.

'Is it something special?' The Princess looked from one boy to the other, whilst impatiently waiting for a reply.

'Well?' Vanadae insisted. 'What have you found, I would very much like to know, immediately!'

'Our apologies, your gracefulness, it is a matter for the King,' said the stable boy. 'We have seen the unmistakable hair of a Golden Unicorn, with tracks leading deep into the Spellbound Woods! The first time…'

Before the stable boy could continue, the Princess jumped and made a high pitch squeal. Rather unbefitting of a Royal, the stable boys thought.

She was filled with uncontrollable excitement and shouted at them, 'Where? Where did you see it? We must find it at once!'

Upon uttering those words, Vanadae sprinted to the castle to tell the King and Prince, like a possessed Dart Hare, which was a bizarre and brilliant magical creature, found only in the Spellbound Woods.

The stable boys were somewhat aggrieved by this, as they hoped they would have the chance to gain some sort of recognition from King Magnus the Mighty for finding traces of the highly prized Golden Unicorn.

Their time would come, they thought after some contemplation, and headed back down to the Royal Stables, awaiting the inevitable arrival of the King and his Kingsmen for the Royal Golden Hunt.

Vanadae finally found her father and brother deep

inside the Royal Armoury, and she could not wait to tell them the news. After Vanadae had blurted out the fact there were tracks of the Golden Unicorn, she continued, 'Father, please allow me to follow the tracks and ensure they are…'

But before Vanadae could finish her request, the King held up a stern hand to establish silence. He then stood with a momentary awestruck astonishment, then finally bellowed to his King's Guard, 'Men, prepare for the Royal Golden Hunt. We will finally have the crowning trophy of them all — a Golden Unicorn horn.

This is our chance to stop those petulant rulers of Ovamthia and Valastry from entering these lands in search of the cursed creature. All they want is part of my Kingdom so they can no doubt supplant me and take Theos for their own. Mark my words, gentlemen, I will see to it that we capture and slay the beast first!'

Vanadae realised there and then what a fool she had been. If only she had kept it a secret from her bloodthirsty father and asked the stable boys to lead her to the tracks, the Golden Unicorn may well have still been safe, and she could have found it and ensured no one else found it.

In shock and disgust at King Magnus the Mighty's response to this news, Vanadae asked with tears streaming down her face, 'Please, Father, you must know how much I have always wanted to see a Golden Unicorn, please do not do this, we must protect it!'

The mighty King looked down past his huge belly, adorned with the Royal Crest of Theos and replied, 'Vanadae, you forget yourself, my daughter. You know what this means.

We must be the first Splendanians to kill this creature. It is the only magical trophy I need to ensure my rule over Valastry and Ovamthia.

Each of the realms would take this horn as their right to rule over all others. Without this trophy, we will be vulnerable to more attacks by armies looking to overthrow us and cast us out of our palace.

Do you not see? We need to claim this horn. One day, you will have to make a decision such as this when you rule over Splendania.'

Vanadae managed a cruel laugh, and said with venom, 'I would rather denounce myself from this family and live on the peaks of Dagger Falls than allow you to harm a unicorn. Though I have not seen one, they are dear to me above all else, and I will protect them from you.'

King Magnus the Mighty looked furious, as his King's Guard and Galderon all stood in stunned silence at this outburst.

'You will accompany me and my King's Guard on the Royal Golden Hunt, and you will have no choice but to watch as we take what is rightfully ours.

This is my kingdom, and I will ensure my rule. Now, get your things at once, Vanadae!' King Magnus the Mighty sharply retorted, throwing his hand vigorously toward the giant doorway, as Vanadae ran from the Royal Armoury, in tears.

The King, now redder in the face than ever, then turned to his King's Guard and demanded loudly, 'Make sure my horse Svaldrim is armoured and well-fed. Prepare to leave at midday!'

The palace staff and King's Guard all leapt into action from their King's command and began to prepare immediately.

This was a most bittersweet command from the King, as Vanadae had always dreamt of exploring the Spellbound Woods of Theos.

Queen Katarina was known for her encapsulating tales of the magical creatures that dwelled within these far-reaching and unexplored woods. There were also stories about the momentous monuments built by people or creatures lost to time that she had always hoped to visit and learn more about.

These tales of legendary creatures and places filled Vanadae with excitement and wonder; she had always wondered whether she would find and gaze upon an ancient Pillar of Pixies, the mystical River of Stone, or even the Flying Waterfall where the water would flow mysteriously and spectacularly upwards.

There were creatures that she had learnt about that she wished to find and protect, like her most beloved Golden Unicorn, which was known by the lucky few to lay eyes on her, said to glimmer like blinding starlight.

But the thought of her father and the King's Guard all trying relentlessly to kill this animal on what should have been a fantastical journey tore at her heart like a ruthless dagger.

Vanadae, still in anguish and pain from the King's decision, ran to the Palace Gardens to find Queen Katarina and tell her what had happened. Knowing that her mother would give her advice and support, Vanadae explained what she had foolishly told the King, and what the King had cruelly demanded of her.

Queen Katarina the Paladin gently embraced Vanadae as only mothers would, and spoke softly, 'Oh, my daughter, do not despair. You must be stronger now more than ever before.

Your father can be so close-minded at times, forgetting that not all of us desire to hunt all things living and misunderstood. But you must go on the Hunt, trust in your brother, and keep him from harm.

I feel that many things are not how they appear at this moment, and before the journey is over, I am convinced your father will see the beauty in the unicorns and your love for them, and above all else, for you.'

Vanadae looked up at the beautiful Queen's face and smiled, 'I will go, Mother. And I will keep Galderon safe, I promise. I will make Father, and all of Theos, see the beauty and magic of what they hunt by the end, even if it's the last thing I do!'

Queen Katarina escorted Vanadae to the palace courtyard where the King's Guard and Palace staff were rushing around, packing their weapons and supplies onto the horses and carts.

Magnus the Mighty did his best to ignore Vanadae's piercing gaze as she walked into the Palace to begin packing. With a heavy heart, the King approached Queen Katarina and told her the plans to finally gain the Golden Unicorn trophy.

Queen Katarina was in a precarious position as to being supportive and excited for King Magnus to claim what he had desired for years, but also in despair as to Vanadae's feelings about unicorns, and what seeing her father slay one may do to their relationship.

After some time, Vanadae appeared back in the Royal Courtyard with a packed satchel fastened around her shoulders, looking extremely upset and reluctant.

The King was speaking with Queen Katarina, whilst

feeding his massive horse, Svaldrim. Content that the magnificent stead had eaten all he could in preparation for the Royal Golden Hunt, King Magnus then turned to face the growing number of armoured men and women gathered in the Royal Courtyard to inspect the condition of his Kingsmen.

Everyone looked very eager and excited, as this was a day of special significance for them all. To be invited to not only a Royal Hunt but the revered, Royal Golden Hunt, was a great symbol of honour for each of them.

'Galderon!' the King boomed. 'Where is that boy? He is never where he should be when he should be! He will learn a great deal from this hunt if he is to lead his own Royal Hunts when he is of age.'

Just as the King had finished talking to no one in particular, Galderon ran out of the palace doorway with a long and beautifully decorated blue cloak with gold lining.

He looked rather mischievous and heavy-footed, Vanadae thought inwardly; it was as though he was hiding something within his cloak.

Galderon approached the King, trying his best to look prepared and excited. Queen Katarina kissed Galderon and Vanadae on the cheeks and wished them a safe journey then reminded King Magnus, 'Do not get too carried away this time.

Stay away from river dragons, as you may not be so lucky a second time,' with an affectionate wink and a smile.

'Keep our children safe, I beg of you,' Queen Katarina added as she returned to the Palace, having quite enough disturbance for one day.

The Royal Palace's courtyard was buzzing with activity; stable boys, palace staff and Kingsmen were darting in all directions, ensuring they had everything they needed for the journey.

Galderon was overly excited to see all the different weapons that the King's Guard mounted to their horses, and their splendid shining armour glinting in the late morning sun.

Vanadae, however, stood with her arms crossed and a frown on her face as she was both devastated at the fact that she was being forced to join a hunt for her favourite magical creature, and excited to finally lay eyes on a Golden Unicorn.

Who knows what else I may see in the Spellbound Woods? she thought to herself.

The old Sage and Royal Advisor, Rammir the Cunning, so named for his often-magical way of predicting future events correctly, and battle strategy, joined the rabble of excitable hunters.

He stood next to Vanadae quietly and then nudged her arm with his elbow.

Vanadae looked up, and a gleaming smile sprang to her face. She said loudly, 'Rammir my old friend, I'm so happy you're coming with us. This bunch of brainless oafs could do with your wise counsel, and I could do with at least one person not sneering at my distaste for harming beautiful, innocent creatures!'

Her voice rose as she spoke. Evidently, her words were aimed at her father. Whether he heard her words or not was a mystery, as he did not react.

Rammir responded in his deep and authoritative voice, 'Vanadae, my dear Princess, although we set out to kill this pure creature, I believe that it may do more harm to your father in the end.

What form that will be in, I cannot say. Unicorns are not to be meddled with lightly, and if this Golden Unicorn is indeed real and not an old wife's tale, then I stand with you in protecting her, if I can.

But I would rather that fact stayed between us Princess, as you of all people know, it could get me into serious trouble,' he whispered with a cheeky half-smile.

Vanadae laughed and patted her mahogany brown pony, Whisper, with affection.

The King was concluding his final checks on his

beautiful and colossal horse, Svaldrim. He mounted up using a stunning footstool of red and gold, and declared to the huntsmen and women, 'We journey forth as the first Splendanians ever to finally slay the Golden Unicorn and ensure the Royal House of Theos remains in power.

Ride now my brothers in arms, for the glory of Theos.'

~ Chapter 3 ~

The Spellbound Woods

With a menacing roar from the Kingsmen that echoed loudly within the Royal Courtyard, Vanadae and Galderon were both helped up onto their ponies, and their journey began.

The Golden Hunt had finally started by the King leading the hunting party down the dazzling white paved flagstones that covered the Palaces entrance, and out through the nearby town of Vinlimare.

With high pointed rooftops and beautifully decorated trees lining the paved Royal Road, Vinlimare was shadowed by the high, jaw-dropping Palace.

The town was filled with adoring Splendanians that lined the streets, bidding their good luck and wishes to

King Magnus, Princess Vanadae and Prince Galderon, whilst throwing roses and lavender at the feet of the horses. The Royal Golden Hunt was the talk of the town. When everyone heard that a Golden Unicorn had been sighted, excitement spread throughout Theos.

When they finally reached the town's end, they followed the Royal Road for miles and miles until they reached the fringes of the Spellbound Woods.

Excitement and nervousness were rife within the hunting party, especially within Vanadae. She could not help but be in awe of the dark, momentous Woods that lay before her, but at the same time, she felt scared and alone.

Galderon, however, was side by side with King Magnus, and he looked on in wonder at the sight of the Spellbound Woods.

He had never been outside the palace grounds before. With the dizzying thoughts of adventure and the opportunity to prove himself all spinning in his head, he had no time to notice Vanadae's anguish.

Rammir the Cunning, sensed that Vanadae was not herself, so he rode up next to the beautiful Princess and said softly, 'Do not be afraid, your Highness. You will see truly extraordinary things in this forest, but know this, in the end, I doubt any harm will come to you or your beloved Golden Unicorn.

I must warn you, however, there is magic at work in these woods, and you shouldn't wander off alone, especially at night.'

'What will we see Rammir?' Vanadae asked whilst staring straight at the forest entrance in motionless contemplation. 'For years, I have dreamt of finding the Lost Pillars of Pixies. I remember the tales that you told me as a child, that they can only be seen at night by a happy chance, and that they disappear and move once seen, and that they leave a marked Pixie Pebble to take.

Can this be true? I would very much like to find one at least in my lifetime. Will I ever see them, Rammir?'

'I cannot say,' Rammir responded quickly. 'You may find yourself gazing upon things that you dare not believe, but worry not my dear, you are well protected.

Now, let us continue onwards, your Highness. The Spellbound Woods await us.'

The King and his mighty horse, Svaldrim, led the way into the Spellbound Woods with the two stable boys who first sighted the Golden Unicorn hair and tracks walking by his side.

King Magnus the Mighty brought them along to ensure they led the Royal Golden Hunt on the right path, which they did without question. They also felt redeemed as this was their reward, stolen from them by an eager

Vanadae.

They hurried through the thick forest entrance and retraced their steps to the unmistakable hoofprints and golden hair that was brushed against a tall tree.

'Here, your Majesty, this is what we found. Surely, the hair of a Golden Unicorn.'

The Golden Hunt all gathered around the tree to catch a glimpse of the golden hair, and sure enough, they were all convinced and confident that their hunt would end with victory.

King Magnus the Mighty held out his hand to suggest the stable boy place the golden hair in his palm, which he did without thinking.

'Yes...there is no mistaking this, the King said menacingly, whilst staring at the golden strands of hair in his hand. 'We will find and slay the beast, once and for all. Follow me, we are on the right path. The Golden Unicorn must be near.'

Vanadae tried to hide the disgust on her face unsuccessfully. She could not see why this was all happening, or why indeed a Golden Unicorn horn was the assurance her father needed to rule his kingdom.

As she passed the tree with the golden hair, she pulled a strand and held it to her heart, closing her eyes, as if to make a wish, and then put it away in her cloak.

With excitement in the air, the Kingsmen all started moving forward whilst chattering about how best the King would slay the beast. They followed an old and rugged path through the Spellbound Woods for hours, catching sight of hoofprints and golden hair caught on low broken and snapped branches.

Rammir the Cunning was riding alongside Vanadae, and they spoke of ancient places, battles, and creatures, which she loved to do to pass the time.

Vanadae was known for her somewhat cheeky and endearing curiosity, so it was no surprise when she asked Rammir outright; 'Just how long have you been the Sage in my father's court, Rammir? It must be getting on a fair few...decades? Dare I say?'

With a scoff of both delight and amusement at Vanadae's questioning, Rammir the Cunning responded, 'Oh goodness, no one has ever asked me that, or indeed had the sheer courage, shall we say before...and do you know my dear Princess, I've completely lost track of the years. It feels like it must be centuries!

And judging by my dwindling appearance, it surely must be!' He then winked at Vanadae to suggest he was joking about his unnatural lifespan and service to the King.

'But enough about my lack of youthfulness,' Rammir said, trying to change the subject. 'We will soon be approaching the Flying Waterfall, my Princess. Listen carefully, there is some speculation that it was here that a massive magical battle took place many decades ago, between a Witch and the long-forgotten Wizard of the Woods, Elzagron — the likes of which have not been seen for an age.'

Vanadae turned in sudden amazement to look at Rammir, listening intently to his next words as they advanced through the deepening forest.

Rammir continued, knowing Vanadae was surely enraptured. 'There are those that believe the Flying Waterfall remains as a result of the sheer magical force used during the vicious and preternatural combat of the Witch and Wizard.

A magnificent array of spells and magical attacks were used from both parties, laying waste to the surrounding area that you will shortly see with your own eyes.

It is also where your father defeated Bildris, deep down in the caverns below — and even that seems like a lifetime ago,' Rammir explained to Vanadae excitedly, wondering how she would react to this remarkable tale whilst also reflecting, noticeably, at how old he was, with a sigh of acceptance.

Ignoring the tale of her father and Bildris deliberately, Vanadae asked hurriedly, 'An ancient magical battle happened in these woods, and there was a

Wizard and a Witch who lived and fought here too?

What kind of nonsense is that, Rammir?' Vanadae rudely inquired with a dry laugh, disbelieving everything Rammir the Cunning had said.

Rammir did not reply; instead, he simply looked forward in a state of remembrance almost, it seemed to Vanadae.

This gave Vanadae more time to process this astonishing information. A few minutes went by as they got closer and closer to the Flying Waterfall.

Vanadae asked more politely this time, as burning curiosity got the better of her, 'So, what happened to the Wizard Elzagron? Why did they fight each other? And where are they now? I'm afraid I won't believe it until I see this so-called Flying Waterfall.'

'This tale is known to the King and Queen and most of Splendania, my Princess. Your mother keeps ancient texts in the Royal Library that suggest the Witch and Wizard were both responsible for casting a terrible, malicious spell upon the Lake of Wishes out of spite, to repay the Royal families for mistreating them many years ago.

The Lake of Wishes is where the so-called Golden Wishes are made Once in a Lifetime, to the members of the Royal Family; it was an evil parting gift from the pair before their departure.

It is thought that Elzagron was not eager to be partied to this magic, as he knew what a terrible curse laid within the spell.'

Rammir looked at Vanadae with sincere and troubled eyes and continued, 'Be warned Your Highness, there has not been a Golden Wish made or granted for generations, as the fear that surrounds making it is still rife with all who know the harrowing tale of your great grandmother, Queen Thipthania.'

Rammir then paused, staring into the atmosphere, as if he were recollecting in subdued remorse.

Vanadae, understandably in shock, asked, 'Do the Golden Wishes exist? I thought they were just an old legend used to keep children from the dangers of wishing for needless things. Tell me, Rammir, what happened to the Queen, and why was she the last to make a Golden Wish?'

'To be granted the Golden Wish, it is believed that you must give something in return, your Highness. In this case, Queen Thipthania…'

Rammir the Cunning stopped briefly to contemplate his next words carefully, so as not to frighten Vanadae.

'It is known that she wished too greedily, and the legend is that her unexplained madness and untimely death was the Witch's punishment. I shall say no more.'

It appeared to Vanadae that Rammir uttered these last words in peculiar resentment as if he had some sort of personal connection to this tale.

Lost in deep thought and conversation, the Golden Hunt had reached the magnificent, bewildering Flying Waterfall.

The Kingsmen all stopped and stared in astonishment at the sight of the waterfall, where the water flowed upwards from a deep canyon full of river beasts. It was here in the canyon that King Magnus the Mighty earned his Special, by defeating the monstrous River Dragon, Bildris.

The water flowed up from the canyon, and to the surface, where they stood as a narrow stream. Vanadae hurried to the front of the hunting party to the side of Galderon, who was staring in silence at the peculiar upside-down waterfall.

'Can you believe your eyes, Vanadae? How can this be?' Galderon asked, trembling in wonder.

'The Witch and Wizard of the Woods had an epic magical duel here, centuries ago, and caused all of this magic upon the waterfall. They say that the Witch destroyed the Wizard, Elzagron, and she is still hiding somewhere in the woods.

She grants wishes for a terrible price. She may even be watching us at this very moment,' Vanadae responded with a contumelious grin on her face, knowing that Galderon would believe it.

However, she was under the impression that Rammir's tale of the Witch, Elzagron and the Golden Wishes was in fact, a load of rubbish.

Galderon had a nervous look on his face as he did indeed believe the exaggerated rendition of Rammir's tale and was now worried a Witch was following and watching them. Galderon was a very impressionable boy; Vanadae knew this, and so she exploited it most of the time for fun.

As they continued through the Spellbound Woods, they passed endless tall trees and heard loud mysterious creature noises that sounded in the dark.

They followed the winding streams and old pathways littered with peculiarly shaped ruins of ornate stone, whilst the sun was going down.

Something amazingly fast caught Vanadae's eye; she looked suddenly at a nearby tree and saw for the first time, a husk of Dart Hares.

These large white hares were known for leaping impossibly vertically up the trees from one to another, hopping along the branches, and acting similarly to squirrels; this was very odd, given the size of the Dart

Hares.

Vanadae loved seeing these bizarre and wonderful creatures playing peacefully amongst themselves. She hoped to see more as her journey continued.

The woods became very dark very quickly, but this was the most magical time in the Spellbound Woods, for the lights of the elusive fairies glowed and sparkled just out of reach, lighting up the pretty and strange flowers of the forest floor.

King Magnus the Mighty ordered two of his best Knights, Anselet and Thimien the Unbreakable, to hunt for deer and for the others to set up a camp for the night. When Vanadae saw Knight Thimien, she asked Rammir the Cunning to explain how he was awarded his Special.

Ever ready to tell a tale, Rammir unravelled the epic tale of how after a Royal Hunt that spanned over one entire year, Thimien was bestowed his Special. The King ordered the killing of a very deadly creature in Valastry — the terrifying Scorpix.

It was known and feared by Splendanians as a giant scorpion found in the Barren Wastes. Thimien the Unbreakable stood alone against this vile creature after all others were too badly hurt to defeat it.

On the rocky and sandy wilds of Valastry, Thimien the Unbreakable's shield was bashed and battered by the

Scorpix's horrifying stinger in defence of his life, but it did not back down until with one lucky strike, Thimien cut clean through its tail and thrust his sword into the beast's protruding mouth, leaving it to stumble and fall from a high rock into its dusty grave.

Vanadae seemed genuinely impressed by a tale of the Royal Hunt for once, and responded to Rammir the Cunning, saying, 'Well, if there was anyone who deserves a Special so grand, it is Thimien the Unbreakable. When all others fell, he stood alone and faced down the poor creature, which, however, would still be alive and not bothering anyone if my father hadn't ordered its demise.'

Soon enough, Knights Anselet and Thimien returned with a huge, dead Silverprong Stag, dressed beautifully with its revered silver antlers and purple streaks lining his magnificence coat on the back of Thimien's horse.

Sir Anselet had slain the creature with a well-placed arrow to the heart. Sir Anselet was a renowned archer, known to perform seemingly impossible tricks with arrows to entertain onlookers.

Vanadae had always wondered whether anyone else even noticed how beautiful these animals were. *Or were they simply a target to shoot arrows at and eat without thought?*

Vanadae and Galderon were wandering around the

edges of the camp, when suddenly, Rammir the Cunning called for them to return to the campfire for their meals. When they arrived at the roaring fire, they felt the warmth, and took comfort in the light as the forest at night was dark, and an uneasy feeling took hold of them both.

They returned to hear the King boast about his many triumphs over magical monsters, and the King's Guard all cheering to the stories they had heard a hundred times over.

Vanadae thought to herself that she could recount the stories for her father, as she had heard them so many times, each time grating on her mind more and more. King Magnus was telling the tale of when he led a Royal Hunt to slay a gallivanting Giant on the fringes of Ovamthia.

Galderon loved this story, as he was always intrigued by Ovamthia and the monsters that dwelled in that faraway realm.

Vanadae, however, thought that there was no need for the King to have slain a peaceful Giant in the first place, let alone retell the tale so distastefully. She hated hearing the misplaced bragging of her father.

Vanadae could not sit and listen to another word, so she shot up from her seat and walked away from the camp into the cold, dark edges of the forest.

There was barely any light where she stood and

looked out to the trees. She saw a glimmer of faded ghostly light moving in the distance.

Could this be one of the fabled Pillar of Pixies, she thought to herself, both afraid and exhilarated at the same time.

As Vanadae peered at the mysterious glowing light, she had the uncontrollable urge to follow it and see if it was a Pillar of Pixies. After hearing about them from Rammir the Cunning, the thought of finding a Pixie Pebble left by the Pixies and following the next apparition of their long-lost Pillars excited her immensely.

Vanadae left the encampment, walking cautiously toward the lights in the trees, feeling incredibly nervous as to what she may find. She had forgotten the wise counsel of Rammir, telling her not to wander alone at night and the warning of the magic that stirred within the forest unseen.

Meanwhile, back at the campfire, Galderon had finished his portion of spit-roasted Silverprong Stag leg and he was enraptured by familiar tales of old and new stirring stories of recent monster hunts.

Galderon was inspired by the strength and bravery of the Knights as they told their stories, and he wanted nothing more than to become a brave Knight himself; to one day tell the tales of hunting down the fiercest monsters of the three realms.

He looked past the King to find that Vanadae was missing. Struck with momentary anguish, he found himself on his feet, looking around the camp for his sister. He checked her tent to find no lit torches or signs of her.

Soon, he stumbled across a nearby huntsman and asked, ‘Have you seen Vanadae? She is nowhere in sight, and I fear she may be in danger. You know how she gets when hearing tales of the hunts; she wanders off every time!’

‘Yes, my Lord Galderon. She entered the woods that way, in a trance it seemed, so I thought it best to let her be,’ the Huntsman replied, eager to not disappoint a member of the Royal House.

Galderon hurried in the direction the huntsman gave him, and he entered the dark of the forest with a torch lighting his way.

Vanadae had been following the glimmering white light for what seemed like an age, and finally, she could see a spectral vision of a beautiful, towering, and thin elegant tower in the distance, glowing blue and white. She could hear high-pitched voices laughing and frolicking from within.

‘Can this be?’ she asked herself aloud. ‘I have found one! Who else can say they’ve seen a Pillar of Pixies in their lifetimes!’

As soon as she spoke, she became aware of how far she had wandered alone and hoped she could find her way back. With thoughts of wonder and fear twirling in her head, she continued forward, towards the astonishing Pillar of Pixies.

The voices grew louder, and then suddenly, all went quiet. The Pillar disappeared in a blue flash. In shock and alarm at the sudden darkness, she turned around and saw Galderon approaching quickly towards her.

'There you are, Vanadae. What on earth possessed you to walk so far away from camp?' Galderon asked in trepidation.

'Galderon did you see? The Pillar of Pixies! I found one; it was just there. I could even hear them!' Vanadae responded excitedly, pointing at nothing Galderon could see. 'You must have scared them off, you foolish boy. Now, how will I find the next one?'

'A Pillar of what? Come back to the camp Vanadae, it is not safe in these woods, especially at night. Remember what Rammir told you!'

Vanadae ignored Galderon's pleas and rushed to where the ethereal Pillar stood, remembering that they were fabled to leave a marked Pixie Pebble where the Pillar was last seen.

Galderon hurried to her side, finding it very strange

how Vanadae was frantically searching the forest floor.

'Here – they left one for me. The tales are true, Galderon. Look!' Vanadae held out her hand, holding an immaculately smooth white stone with a stunningly engraved rune on the one side; a shape like Vanadae had never seen.

'What is this? What does it mean, Vanadae?' Galderon asked in shock at the sight of something so peculiar and magical.

'This is a Pixie Pebble,' Vanadae explained excitedly. 'Left by the Pixies for me – I cannot believe it. Rammir was right! I must take this to him at once.'

Vanadae looked around and back to Galderon, who was staring with a perplexed look on his face at Vanadae.

'Now, how do we get back? I have no idea where we are.'

Vanadae followed Galderon back to the camp whilst explaining how she happened to find the Pillar of Pixies, what Rammir had told her about leaving a Pixie Pebble to take to the next Pillar, and how she believed that one day, she would find the entrance to the Lost City of Pixies that must surely exist and be seen only to those who collect all of the Pixie Pebbles.

What could be within? Galderon and Vanadae pondered. *Magic? Treasure? Ancient knowledge?*

Perhaps all of these things, she thought. One day, she hoped to find out.

When Galderon and Vanadae arrived back at the warm fire, Rammir caught Vanadae's gaze and approached her, sensing that she had seen something in the forest.

'Well, my dear Princess, what tales of wonder do you have for me?' Rammir asked inquisitively, but with certainty that he already knew the answer, as was his custom.

'Rammir, look...they chose me, I saw with my own eyes a Pillar of Pixies,' she answered softly and pulled from her beautiful green and golden cloak the bewildering Pixie Pebble that shone a brilliant pure white.

In astonishment, Rammir congratulated Vanadae but warned her this quest would take her far into each realm, and it must be kept a secret for now.

Filled with fascination and musings at the opportunity that was before her, Vanadae fell into a deep sleep in her tent whilst staring longingly at the Pixie Pebble in her hand, resting on her pillow.

~ CHAPTER 4 ~

DANGERS FROM THE DEEP

The sun broke through the trees to awaken Vanadae, who was still snoozing away in her tent, dreaming of faraway places both hot and cold.

The spirited songs of Bright Tails and other mysterious sounds echoed around the encampment from the deep thickness of the surrounding forest. This was much to Vanadae's delight as she slowly roused herself out of her tent, looking around vaguely to catch the sight of Galderon or Rammir the Cunning.

Before long, Vanadae found Galderon enthusiastically chomping down on bread and cheese next to the morning fire.

Not surprising, thought Vanadae inwardly, as she knew if there was food and warmth to be had, Galderon would have it.

'So, today is the day, isn't it, Galderon? When you finally become a famous hunter and slayer of the elusive, precious and magical Golden Unicorn!' Vanadae spoke with an air of joviality as she mocked her brother.

'Who knows, Vanadae, perhaps I will slay more than one!' Galderon responded hastily, taking Vanadae off guard somewhat, as usually, he would not retaliate in this manner.

'There is only one Golden Unicorn, Galderon,' Vanadae retorted viciously. 'And I will ensure no harm comes to it, mark my words! There is absolutely no reason for us to be hunting something so innocent and beautiful. Do not become like Father, I beg of you.'

Galderon took these words with a heavy heart, as it was indeed his desire to become like his father; but he could also sense the absolute despair in Vanadae.

Rammir the Cunning approached Vanadae and Galderon whilst patting breadcrumbs from his long brown and intriguingly decorated beard.

'Ah, the Royal children of House Theos. Come, the stable boys and trackers have King Magnus in a state of unfounded purpose, as the tracks lead on not far from here, and he is eager to finally find the poor creature.

Perhaps we really might gaze upon the wondrous Golden Unicorn on this day.'

Reluctantly, Vanadae packed her travel bag ready to join the Golden Huntsman, ensuring the Pixie Pebble was safe, lying perfectly smooth and unnaturally pearlescent, hidden at the bottom.

The Keeper of the Horses arrived to hand over Whisper, Vanadae's loyal and silky-smooth brown-haired pony, along with Volheim, Galderon's larger and steadfast, shiny black coated pony.

After several hours of riding deeper into the Spellbound Woods, passing overgrown ruins of ancient dwellings and mysterious, colourful flowers covering the ground, they found themselves blocked by felled trees, heaped untidily on the narrow path between giant boulders adorned with vibrant green hanging moss, making it impossible to pass.

King Magnus the Mighty ordered Sir Anselet to inspect the fallen trees, as he suspected this blockage was no accident. At the same time, he commanded the King's Guard to arm themselves, and for Rammir the Cunning to protect Princess Vanadae and Prince Galderon.

Panic and fear suddenly took hold of Galderon and Vanadae. They had never seen their father so battle-ready and commanding; they feared they may come to harm from whatever he was concerned about, and they had no reason to doubt his apprehension, as they were more than aware of how many battles he had seen and won.

'My King, these trees did not fall willingly,' Sir Anselet explained with a mixture of mild trepidation and excitement, tightening his grip on his elegant bow. 'It looks to be a trap, set by the Grey Goblins. As evident from the markings, their ugly axes have felled these trees. We must go around or prepare for an attack.'

'Goblins be damned! Foolish creatures so eager for a fight when they have never succeeded against men!' roared King Magnus the Mighty into the surrounding air to warn the Goblins that he was ready for battle with them.

'This day is no different, Goblin scum! Face us, you cowards, emerge from the depths where you cower and scheme!' he bellowed upwards.

And with this, the King's Guard formed ranks, swords, and shields in hand to protect the King at the front of the Golden Hunting party.

Meanwhile, Rammir the Cunning instinctively and quickly escorted a nervous Vanadae and a thrilled Galderon, eager to witness his first battle, back to a safe distance. He never for one second took his eyes off Vanadae.

The loud clattering of iron axes, indistinctive groans and menacing voices grew louder and louder above them on the narrow cliffs. Galderon gasped in fear at the sight of the grotesque grey and scarred skin of the ugly and short gang of Goblins, all shouting threateningly whilst hurling rocks at the King and his men.

With a swift arrow to the neck and a sharp cry of pain, the first Goblin was shot from his perch by Sir Anselet, and it fell into the ravine.

One after the other, the Goblins fell, struck with swift and unforgiving arrows. A brave few jumped onto the Knight's horses, only to be skewered by heavy steel swords, with the King slaying as many as he could reach.

Galderon had never seen such fury and bloodlust. He was both enthralled at the sight of battle and afraid for his father's life. Vanadae could not watch, and in terror, she held onto Rammir's arm tightly, with her eyes closed, whilst he covered her with his long black and crimson cloak and clutched his long walking stick evermore tightly in preparation to defend Vanadae and Galderon.

A cry of agony from one of the King's Guard echoed from the scintillating skirmish. Blood seeped from his shoulder, covering his silver armour and onto his horse.

A Goblin had managed to pierce his armour with a quick and furious swipe with its hideously jagged axe whilst letting out a horrifyingly high-pitched laugh. At the sound of a spear being launched, there was a sudden thud on the ground.

Vanadae could hear the cries of anguish and unknown words of dispersing Grey Goblins, signifying the end of the battle, whilst the cheers of celebration and victory surrounded her.

The last Goblin had been run through with Thimien the Unbreakable's elegant spear, hurled with untold ferocity to save his fellow knight who had been injured seconds before.

Where the defeated gang of Goblins retreated was unknown to all who entered the Spellbound Woods, it was generally believed they lurked in cold and dark caverns deep below the forest floor, and only they knew the entrances.

They were far too spritely to follow, and all who encountered them alone either did not live to tell the tale or dared not go after them.

King Magnus the Mighty was loud in victory, giving enthusiastic pats on the shoulders to his men as they cheered for him.

When the King had finally had his fill of gratification, he soon remembered his young children were present in the forest and quickly raised his voice to enquire, 'Rammir my old friend, are you still living? Have my children fled, or are they safe in your company?'

'Father, you killed so many of those vile creatures! I cannot wait until I can join you in a battle. That was exhilarating! Can I become a Knight? Father, please?' Galderon asked energetically whilst looking over at the Knights as they piled the dead Goblins in a high, ugly mound of grey skin and purple blood.

'Ah, my dear boy, soon, you will be of age and accompany me on many adventures where we will fight side by side! I trust Vanadae is well protected, Rammir?' the King asked reluctantly, still reeling from Vanadae's outburst at the Palace that embarrassed him.

Rammir the Cunning lifted his cloak gently, revealing Vanadae still gripping his arm.

'I would never let anything happen to Vanadae, my King. I have and will always do my duty to protect the noble house of Theos and its lineage,' Rammir said whilst looking into Vanadae's tearful eyes, still very afraid from the battle.

The King turned around, now satisfied that his children were safe and thundered at his men, 'Great songs will be sung of your aim, Anselet. No man alive has a truer shot. Now come, we ride onwards! Let us not forget our purpose in this forsaken forest. The Golden Unicorn is within our grasp! We will soon be approaching the Enchanted Rocks of Elianth. Keep your guard up!'

With that, the Golden Hunt resumed. They passed over the bloodied bodies of the slain Grey Goblins, heaped into an unsightly mess of a mound.

Wanderers of the Spellbound Woods would usually steer clear of the Enchanted Rocks of Elianth, for there was a dark and harrowing tale regarding the beings that used to dwell there.

It was believed that what happened to the Order of Elianth - a bygone group of Witches and Wizards - was so evil, that a curse now dwelled upon this place.

Not much was known about the Order of Elianth, but most knew it was ripped apart by the rulers of each realm for personal gain and blood-sport.

The Golden Hunt continued ever deeper through the Spellbound Woods, still overly pleased with themselves for winning the battle with the Grey Goblins. Vanadae rode in silence, pondering at the sights of the forest.

Beautiful colours surrounded them from tall and peculiar trees and flowers as far as the eye could see. So caught up in this beauty, she had almost forgotten what she was doing there.

Before long, she was swiftly removed from her daydreaming when Rammir the Cunning approached her to say, 'The entrance to the Cave of Eternity, your Highness,' suggestively nodding in the direction of an enormous, dark gateway into shadow. 'So deep and far-reaching, no one has ever seen what awaits at its end, as none that has entered has returned, it is said.'

'One day perhaps, I will reach the end and find hidden creatures that have never been seen before. Maybe it is a gateway to another realm or hidden land we know not of yet. I wish to be the first to reach its secrets and return triumphant!' Vanadae vowed to Rammir.

~ CHAPTER 5 ~

THE COURAGE OF BROTHERS

The stable boys and trackers suddenly became excited and ran forward, following hoof prints, and eagerly told King Magnus the Mighty they must be near to the Golden Unicorn.

The trees became sparser, and they approached a huge clearing in the forest, surrounded by gigantic trees, stretching so high up that they could not see the top.

Vanadae and Galderon both rode up to the front of the pack, next to the King. They were all staring in astonishment at what was in front of them — the wondrous majesty of a Golden Unicorn, gleaming in beautiful golden light in the darkness.

A flowing golden mane draped from her proud and

steadfast neck, and her horn protruding from her elegant head was of pure gold.

Vanadae could hardly contain her excitement. She quickly leapt from atop her pony and rushed in the direction of the Golden Unicorn.

Startled by the sudden noise and commotion from the quiet of the forest, the Unicorn became frightened and darted in circles, trying to escape the sunken clearing, but could not find a way up the steep verges of rock and mud, and its exit was blocked by the Royal Golden Hunt itself.

The Huntsmen, Galderon and Rammir all watched on, perplexed as to Vanadae's actions, as they all knew they were there to watch the King kill the beast. Loud murmuring began from the Royal Golden Hunt in the confusion, which alarmed the Golden Unicorn even more.

Vanadae headed towards the jaw-droppingly beautiful animal, whilst trying to calm it with her hands reaching out.

'Shhhh, it's ok now I've found you. No harm will come to you, I am your…' she tried petting her.

Before Vanadae could finish her sentence, she found herself on the ground, as King Magnus ferociously pushed her out of the way of his moment of triumph in the most unfatherly manner.

Tears began to stream down Vanadae's face as she could not believe her father would treat her this way just to kill a defenceless, beautiful creature.

Galderon and Rammir both stepped forward in anguish at the sight of the King pushing Vanadae down, as this was no way for a King, a father, or any man to treat a woman, especially one's daughter.

Galderon thought he saw the shape of someone mysterious peering from behind a tree in the distance. With a second glance, there was no sign of them.

The King looked back at Vanadae as she sobbed in the dirt, whilst he approached the Golden Unicorn, pulling his mighty silver great sword from its stunningly decorated sheath.

This signified his intentions to the Golden Hunt. They roared with encouragement from the edges of the muddy cliffs overlooking the clearing, as they were finally about to see a Golden Unicorn be killed, by their King no less.

Vanadae was prepared to do anything to stop any harm coming to the Unicorn, so she wiped her tears, shot up to her feet and ran to the King. Vanadae took hold of his arm to slow him.

But he on the other hand looked down at her and shouted, 'This is our one chance to have our most prized trophy! Unhand me, daughter!'

The King struggled to release himself from Vanadae's tight grip.

Vanadae cried up at the King, 'Can you not see her beauty? She deserves to live in peace, Father, and I will do everything in my power to stop you from harming her.'

The king was bright red with fury at Vanadae's defiance, and as if enchanted by some wicked spell, he threw her down for a second time. Prince Galderon could not take this act of aggression towards Vanadae and rushed to her aid.

The King, so blinded by his bloodlust charged toward the frightened golden light of the Unicorn. The Unicorn now turned to face him and charged with her long, pure golden horn.

King Magnus planted his feet into the ground, and with a swift, low swipe with his great sword, the Unicorn stumbled before Vanadae and Galderon with blood seeping from a gash in her front leg.

In horror and disbelief, Vanadae and Galderon watched their father approach, with a menacing, unrecognisable look on his face, ready for the killing blow.

As soon as King Magnus the Mighty lifted his sword, Kingbreaker, high above his head to strike down powerfully, a loud and violent clash of steel on steel sounded in the clearing, with a dazzling flash of purple erupting from Galderon's sword, Starbolt.

A magical force field knocked King Magnus's great sword out of his hands, and the King, onto his back on the ground, several feet from where he stood before.

Vanadae opened her eyes to see Galderon towering over her and the Unicorn, protecting her by meeting his father's sword in defence with the exquisite shining sword, adorned with beautiful, intriguing markings that were glowing orange, blue and purple down the blade.

Galderon had been hiding it in his cloak all this time; he had taken it from The Royal Armoury just before the Golden Hunt began. Starbolt had given Galderon unnatural strength when wielding it and used a defensive charm to stop the King automatically, almost as if the sword was now one with Galderon and his intentions of using the weapon.

'You will not hurt them again, Father!' Galderon shouted defiantly. 'How could you do this to Vanadae and this poor, beautiful animal, so astounding to behold?' he asked in newfound personal strength, looking down at the injured creature, and Vanadae, who lay with her arms around the Unicorn's neck, weeping.

'Can you not see what you have done? And for what?'

King Magnus the Mighty suddenly emerged from his trance-like state after hearing the powerful words and actions of Galderon. He then crawled onto his knees in atonement for what he had done.

The Golden Hunting party were all silent after watching such a dramatic event unfold, and they were even more confused at the sight of one so Mighty as their King on his knees begging for forgiveness.

Rammir the Cunning approached Vanadae to console her, whilst looking in wonder at the Golden Unicorn lying injured in her arms, panting in pain and distress.

'My King, we must help this poor creature, and you must return to the Palace to consult with the Queen. I have seen it in my mind's eye. We must ensure no one attempts to finish the task we set out to do. Please command a cart to be brought here to carry her back to the Palace to be healed.'

King Magnus the Mighty ordered a cart to the clearing, where the Golden Unicorn lay in pain, blood still gushing from the leg that King Magnus sliced open.

Collectively, ten of the King's strongest men heaved the Unicorn onto the cart. Meanwhile, Vanadae was still by her side, stroking and caring for her; she did not dare take her eyes off her golden beauty.

The King tried to comfort Vanadae, but she would not listen to a word, as this terrible act of her father had severed their love. Rammir the Cunning reminded the King to lead the Golden Hunt back to the Palace as quickly as possible, to save the Golden Unicorn.

'Quickly men, we must return to the Palace! The Royal Golden Hunt is over. We dare not harm the creature any more than I have done. We have been foolish to journey so far into the Spellbound Woods. Follow me home!' King Magnus the Mighty ordered sternly.

As the Golden Hunt departed the dreaded clearing, Vanadae sat on the cart with the Golden Unicorn and tore a large piece of her cloak, then fastened it tightly over the gash in the unicorn's wound.

'It'll be OK I promise you. I will take care of you, and the healers will fix your leg in no time. Please forgive us,' Vanadae said softly, whilst caressing the Golden Unicorn's neck.

Galderon rode alongside the cart, looking cautiously around the ranks of the Golden Huntsmen, as he had a feeling that something was not right. He felt the need to guard Vanadae and the Golden Unicorn now that he had been imbued with untold strength by virtue of his mesmerising sword, Starbolt.

They rode quickly and quietly back through the Spellbound Woods, passing the vast number of peculiar sights they had seen on the way.

This time, however, there was no excitable chattering or contemplation about the history of these long-forgotten places.

The King kept looking back in anguish from the front of the Royal Golden Hunt at Vanadae and the Golden Unicorn, with an overwhelming feeling of guilt and sorrow.

He wondered to himself how he could make this right. Then he remembered he must quickly consult with Queen Katarina the Paladin; she would know what to do, as always.

Rammir the Cunning was walking on the other side of Vanadae and the Unicorn, silently reflecting on what had happened. He cared deeply for Vanadae as if she were his own child; he too was guarding her without her knowledge.

'Vanadae, everything will be all right now. I will not allow you or her to be harmed again,' Galderon leaned over and whispered to Vanadae.

'Thank you, Galderon,' Vanadae responded, still with tears in her eyes as she examined the sword, Starbolt. 'There are no words I can say that will do my gratefulness justice. You saved her life; how can I ever repay you? And where did you find such a glorious weapon?'

'There is nothing to repay, I did what any brother would do. You'd have surely done the same for me,' said Galderon with a smile, looking into Vanadae's eyes. 'I found this sword in Father's armoury; I couldn't leave without it. Something powerful within it feels as if it is meant for me to carry…' Galderon continued, whilst looking down upon Starbolt. 'It's hard to explain.'

'We must discover more about this sword once we return,' said Vanadae. 'Maybe Rammir has some books about the weapons of ancient wars. Or perhaps Mother knows of its origin. We'll know soon enough, I hope.'

After hours of riding, they could see the Spellbound Wood's end. All of the Kingsmen were disheartened by this Golden Hunt, for they had finally managed to find and trap a Golden Unicorn, but not fulfil the Golden Hunt's purpose of slaying her and taking the Golden Horn.

Sir Anselet rode up to the King and could not help but ask. 'My Lord, is it not our duty to kill this creature now that we have it in our possession? We have travelled far, and now to return without slaying it seems a terrible waste. How will you ensure your rule over the three kingdoms without accomplishing this?'

'No, Sir Anselet, you ignorant fool. I have spared the life of the Golden Unicorn for it is more important than allowing my children to hate me forever.

I will not allow any more harm to come to this

animal, and you would be wise to ensure none of my men gets any ideas of taking its life either. Do you understand me?' the King replied in anger.

Sir Anselet was taken aback by this change in the King. For he knew only of the King's love for hunting and killing magical creatures across the lands of Splendania.

He did, however, accept his King's wishes, and returned to his position in the Golden Hunt, feeling rather bashful.

The Royal Golden Hunt finally emerged from the dark of the Spellbound Woods into the brisk open air and light of the sun. Vanadae felt a great amount of relief as she was worried throughout the whole journey home that the Golden Unicorn would perish, or that the horrible Grey Goblins would again attack them.

Thankfully, she thought, they were nearing the Palace and the healers.

When the Golden Hunt passed through the high gates of Vinlimare, Splendanians lined the streets once more to catch a glimpse of the King and dctermine whether they had been successful or not.

They were confused as to the demeanour of the King and Kingsmen, for they looked saddened and downtrodden.

One of the citizens caught sight of Vanadae and the

dazzling gold of the Unicorn's coat. 'They have killed the beast! Long may Magnus the Mighty rule over Splendania!' he shouted, followed by rousing applause from the people of Vinlimare.

Vanadae looked up, appalled by hearing this, and stood on the cart over the Golden Unicorn.

'The absurd Royal Golden Hunt has failed in its attempt to mindlessly kill a Golden Unicorn,' said Vanadae scoldingly. 'Behold the wonder of such a majestic animal. The old alliances and prizes for this animal's trophy can be shattered into pieces, for none shall hunt or kill a Golden Unicorn whilst I draw breath!'

With gasps of shock from the on-looking citizens at this powerful statement from their Princess, the gasps and murmurs shortly turned into the sound of clapping and encouragement.

The King watched and listened to Vanadae in astonishment at her unyielding love for this creature. With a small smile of pride and understanding, he turned to face his Palace and commanded the Royal Golden Hunt to continue home, for the Unicorn was still very much in pain and needed aid.

They finally reached the Royal Stables, and King Magnus the Mighty ordered the healers to him at once. The same Knights helped the Golden Unicorn off the cart and into a spacious pen with straw covering the cold floor.

Vanadae was still by her side, ensuring she was taken care of, whilst the healers, after being momentarily awe-struck by her sheer fantastical beauty, got to work on her deep leg wound.

~ CHAPTER 6 ~

BEWARE THE GOLDEN WISH

King Magnus left Vanadae and Galderon in the Golden Unicorn's pen with the healers without saying a word, as he was still in anguish as to how best to fix his bond with Vanadae.

The rest of the Golden Huntsmen were sorting out their gear and having well-earnt bread and ale from the Palace staff, near the Royal Stables on a tremendously long table filled with wholesome food and goblets of ale.

The King dismounted his colossal horse, Svaldrim, and fed him a bucket of crimson apples whilst thinking deeply. He looked to Rammir the Cunning for counsel, as he knew what he had to do.

'Go to the Queen, your Highness,' said Rammir softly. 'I would have thought she resides at the Lake of Wishes. Ask her what is best to do, but be wary, my King, the answer may cost you dearly.'

With a nod of understanding, the King walked slowly towards the beautiful palace gardens that burst with the vivid colour of the well-tended flowers, and the pleasant humming of bees and butterfly wings.

He felt a quiet sense of purpose here; he knew whatever he had to do to make it right, he would accept at all costs.

King Magnus continued down the spectacular Winding Walkway that curved and swayed this way and that way, all the way down to the Lake of Wishes, a wide body of water ending with steep mountain peaks at the water's edge.

The sun was going down, and the water seemed to glow a vibrant orange in the sun's reflection. He took a moment to gaze upon it, reflecting over how big of a brute he had been, disregarding Vanadae's feelings for the Golden Unicorn, and at how defiant Galderon was in defending her and Vanadae with Starbolt.

Not such a small and impressionable boy anymore, the King thought to himself.

By the shores of the Lake of Wishes, he saw Queen

Katarina, flawlessly beautiful and serene, sitting below the Tree of Truth whilst reading.

As King Magnus approached the Queen, she embraced him tightly, as he could not hold in these emotions any longer; he sobbed softly into her shoulder whilst explaining the events of the Royal Golden Hunt.

The Queen did not judge or say a word, but simply consoled Magnus the Mighty by holding him tightly as only your beloved can.

'How can I fix this, my love?' Magnus the Mighty asked, in between sobs. 'I have been such a fool. Vanadae despises me for how I behaved on the Hunt, and rightly so. But I cannot live with her hatred. What must I do?'

'There is one way, my King,' Queen Katarina the Paladin, told him calmly, wiping away his tears.

She turned and plucked a single white leaf from the Tree of Truth and handed it to King Magnus. 'If her love for you has truly been severed, then the one way is to make a Golden Wish.'

'But my Queen, we know as well as any the dangers of making a Golden Wish,' King Magnus said with apprehension. 'My Grandmother, Queen Thipthania...can I take such a risk as that, knowing what happened to her?

What if something happens to you, Vanadae, Galderon or indeed, me? There is no knowing what sorcery lies upon this so-called Lake of Wishes — good or bad. Is there no other way?'

'What, my King, can be more important than the love of your child?' Queen Katarina asked in earnest. 'You must take the risk, for Vanadae's sake. Your bond must be remade for the future of your Kingdom, it is her destiny to rule and unite the three realms once more.

Whatever happens - good or bad - there will always be a way to mend the sorrow.'

Queen Katarina held Magnus the Mighty's hand and gestured toward the Leaf in his palm. 'Make your Golden Wish and cast it into the water, my love,' Queen Katarina instructed, whilst contemplating the repercussions that may derive from doing such a thing.

The King took the leaf and whispered to its bright white surface close to his lips.

'I, King Magnus the Mighty, make my Golden Wish for the love of my child, Princess Vanadae, to be reforged and to never be broken again.'

The King opened his hand, and the leaf blew swiftly to the water's surface. Golden light filled the water as the leaf sank out of sight.

A flood of emotion suddenly filled Vanadae as she was watching over the Golden Unicorn being healed. She felt a powerful sensation in her heart just as the leaf sank through the water and the golden light turned back to clear water. Suddenly, she had an intense desire to run to her father and embrace him as now, she felt no ill will against the King's actions in the Spellbound Woods.

All Vanadae cared about was holding him, as only daughters do, showing fathers their unequivocal love. The Golden Wish, it seemed, had indeed reforged the King's and Vanadae's love bond.

Rammir noticed Vanadae's change in mood and wondered in horror if a Golden Wish had been granted to the King, and at what price.

Rammir knew in his heart that only a Golden Wish would so suddenly change a person's feelings, especially one as strong as love.

'Knight's Anselet and Thimien the Unbreakable,' Vanadae called out excitedly. 'Keep guard of the Golden Unicorn. Let no one touch her but the healers. I must go to my father at once,' she added, with a gleaming smile.

Then she ran towards the Palace after a final glance at the Golden Unicorn, in the utter enchantment of her golden light filling the stable.

Galderon quickly started to follow, struggling to keep up as he tried to understand what had caused his sister's change of heart. Rammir the Cunning, however, did not smile.

He foresaw something terrible about to happen and followed Vanadae and Galderon up to the Palace, then down to the Winding Walkway, overlooking the Lake of Wishes.

Vanadae stopped to look down over a marble balcony and could see the King and Queen under the Tree of Truth.

Vanadae's smile faded instantly, for she watched in despair the sight of her father, King Magnus the Mighty, stumble into Queen Katarina's arms and onto the floor in pain, clutching his chest.

Rammir the Cunning quickly turned to the direction of the Spellbound Woods, realising the sudden pain of the King must be the price of making a Golden Wish and the evil work of the Witch of the Woods.

Rammir looked up to the sky and spoke to the wind with cruelty, 'Curse you, Zelavaine, you wicked, malevolent crone. There is nowhere you can hide from me if you take his life.'

Vanadae and Galderon ran harder than before in complete despair, down the slopes of the Winding Walkway.

Vanadae fell to her knees, sobbing whilst holding the King's hand, 'Father, what is it? What has happened?' she asked in distress, looking from the Queen to Rammir and back to her pale, befallen father.

King Magnus the Mighty looked upon the beautiful face of his daughter and smiled weakly. He gently wiped away her tears with a sorrowful understanding that he was dying, but a flicker of resolute happiness as the love bond had been reforged between them.

'I'm sorry I hurt you,' King Magnus said softly as his strength failed him. 'We men are such foolish things. I see now what a fool I have been. Forgive me, Vanadae, my beautiful daughter.'

'Rammir, you must do something!' Queen Katarina pleaded. 'What is this cursed magic? This surely is not the price we must pay for the Golden Wish!'

Vanadae turned to face Rammir and begged, 'Please Rammir, you must help! Do something, anything!'

Rammir the Cunning, in anguish and fear, as he had realised the frightfully cursed magic still laid upon the Lake of Wishes, knelt to hold Vanadae's shoulders and said, 'There is nothing I can do, my Princess. This is the work of the Witch, Zelavaine. It cannot be undone, save for another Golden Wish.'

As these words were said, King Magnus gave out his last breath of life to the utter horror of his family and Rammir.

'Then I will make my Golden Wish to bring him

back!' Vanadae responded in desperation at the sight of her dead father. 'Out of my way!'

'NO!' Boomed Rammir the Cunning, stunning Vanadae, Queen Katarina and Galderon into silence and motionlessness.

'You will not make a Golden Wish, my princess,' Rammir commanded. 'And none shall ever again!'

As he spoke, a spiralling cloud of golden, magical mist surrounded Rammir the Cunning and the King, who lay dead on the cold shores of the Lake of Wishes.

Astonished and bewildered, Vanadae, Galderon and Queen Katarina, all embraced each other, sobbing collectively in pure hopelessness.

Rammir the Cunning spoke in a low and powerful tone as if casting a spell from within the golden cloud, 'I return the life of King Magnus the Mighty back to him!

And I swear to end the magic that lies on this lake by taking your wretched life, Zelavaine. I have eluded you for far too long, and your time will now come to an end.

No more harm will come to any Splendanian you attempt to curse.'

Rammir then spoke a language not understood by Queen Katarina, Vanadae or Galderon, all watching and listening in shock, 'Skru tilbake tiden, veram meam forman, revela potestatem!'

When Vanadae, Galderon and Queen Katarina opened their eyes, they bore witness to the sight of Rammir the Cunning emerging from the golden cloud, transformed from his former appearance, dressed now in a splendid blue and silver lined cloak, with a brilliant, long, and white beard, decorated with silver jewels.

He was holding a long brown staff as a bright golden light flickered and faded from its end.

'Father!' Vanadae screamed with overwhelming delight as she fell onto King Magnus's chest and held him so tightly, he very nearly could have died again! 'How can this be, Rammir? How have you brought him back?'

Queen Katarina and Galderon looked upon the face of Rammir the Cunning with great uncertainty but also monumental gratefulness.

They were now unaware of who, or indeed, what, exactly Rammir was. The King held Vanadae as tightly as he had ever done before, crying together in complete joy as to his miraculous revival and the bond of love remade.

Rammir the Cunning stood proudly and faced the onlooking, stunned Royal family, holding on to his staff and announced, 'It is clear I have some explaining to do. Where to begin…' Rammir looked down and shook his head in disbelief as to his next words, whilst Vanadae's stared into his teary eyes.

‘My real name…’ hesitated Rammir. ‘…is Elzagron. The long-lost Wizard of the Woods.’

~ Chapter 7 ~

Revelations

It was several moments before any of the Royal Family could find fitting words in response to the extraordinary magic they had just witnessed.

Not only had King Magnus the Mighty been returned from the dead, but Rammir the Cunning had now revealed himself as the Long-Lost Wizard of the Woods, Elzagron.

This was a lot to take in for all of them, but finally, King Magnus, helped up by Vanadae from the floor, embraced Elzagron tightly as an old friend.

'There are no words that will ever be enough, Elzagron. This debt I owe you can never be repaid.

Whatever you ask of me, you shall have it,' King Magnus the Mighty said boldly, with a tear in his eye.

'My Lord Magnus,' began Elzagron. 'All I require is leave to hunt down the Witch, Zelavaine, and ensure the end of the Golden Wish curse that lies upon this lake.

Zelavaine must have been responsible for enchanting you in the Spellbound Woods. Without Galderon taking action with Starbolt, I fear she would have succeeded in her plan — for you to have killed the Unicorn and Vanadae, under her spell.

She will now undoubtedly be aware of my true form being revealed and the magic I cast to bring you back, reversing her spell. I must act quickly; I know her wicked ways from decades past, and I am certain she will no doubt be eager to find me and wreak havoc if not stopped.

I have hidden from her successfully for an age. Her anger, misuse of power and malevolence forced me to abandon her. I have until now, never had the courage to truly stop her.'

The Royal Family listened in astonished silence; the gentle waves of the Lake of Wishes crashing upon the shore seemed louder than ever before as they stared in awe of Elzagron and his fascinating story.

They were bursting with burning questions as the sun was setting on the shores of the Lake of Wishes. The faint light of faraway stars began to illuminate in the dark blue of the clear evening sky.

'You know this Witch, Elzagron?' asked Vanadae in somewhat disbelief, simultaneously realising that this was the first time she had ever mentioned Rammir the Cunning's true name in her lifetime.

'I did,' replied Elzagron, looking down at the ground in contempt for Zelavaine. 'We were once members of the Order of Elianth, a group of Witches and Wizards dedicated to building sanctuaries for creatures and magical beings throughout Splendania, using our powers collectively for good.

After accomplishing many wonders for many years, a time of woe befell us. Some members of our Order were commanded by the Kings and Queens and petulant Princes of Valastry to be their guards or even forced to battle each other in contests of blood sport.

Our ancient and peaceful order was ripped apart by this senseless and mindless barbarity. I…'

Elzagron stopped as a rush of painful memories filled his mind; memories he wondered if it were too soon to speak of.

'Please Elzagron,' Queen Katarina asked humbly, with a gentle hand upon Elzagron's shoulder. 'Please continue. We must know what became of you and this

Zelavaine Witch. Why were you hiding from her for such a long time? And where are all the other members of the Order of Elianth? I have read about the demise of your Order. You have much to tell us.'

Elazagron knew that he had to explain in full to all of them; it was only fair, considering that he had known that Zelavaine was, in fact, responsible for the Golden Wish being cast upon the Lake of Wishes.

'Zelavaine and I were forced to fight against each other by the hateful and cruel Prince of Valastry, Evithis.

He enjoyed watching the magical battles of the last remaining Witches and Wizards of our order above all other tournaments. It was in this particular power battle between me and Zelavaine that he cheered his last cheer,' Elzagron said with a malicious tone in his voice, never heard by any member of the Royal House of Theos before.

Vanadae did not enjoy this wrathful side to the man and friend she had known all her life, but she continued listening, in fear of what she would hear next.

'You see, Zelavaine and I were deeply and secretly in love,' Elzagron explained. 'The thought of having to force our destructive powers upon each other to harm was far too much to even contemplate.

And so, when we were pushed into that blood-stained arena like animals, with the pathological Prince and his Royal subjects all shouting and hurling their disgusting half-eaten food at us to make us fight, we could not bear the thought of hurting one another.

With the overwhelming anger, we both felt in our bones, we cast a collective spell, causing a ginormous, desecrating explosion. I wanted us to leave immediately and never return, but the rage of Zelavaine grew uncontrollable, and no action, word, or power of mine could quell her thirst for vengeance.'

Queen Katarina the Paladin had a look of horrified anguish on her face as she began to realise what happened next in Elzagron's tale.

She had read historical witness statements as to the events that unfolded in Valastry and the gruesome, barbaric death of Prince Evithis. Elzagron realised the Queen's clarity of thought and he tried to continue speaking, but Queen Katarina interrupted him.

'The Witch, Zelavaine, your beloved, she was the one who destroyed Prince Evithis so inhumanely, wasn't she, Elzagron?' the Queen probed, whilst unsuccessfully hiding her disgust. 'How can you have ever had any love for one so barbaric and wicked?

The accounts of Prince Evithis's death are harrowing; he was made an example of before being killed in the most vicious way imaginable.'

Vanadae and Galderon looked at their mother with fear and shock at her out-of-character tone; they had never seen the Queen speak like that before, with such hatred.

'Your Highness, I did all I could to stop her, but her power grew out of hate and anger for how we were treated; I could do nothing to stop it. With all my heart, I wish I could have, for everything else that followed would never have come to pass.'

Vanadae and Galderon were both still in shock from the unravelling of this story; it was hard for them to hear such a tale from Elzagron. There was nothing they could do but listen alongside their mother and father.

'What happened next, Elzagron?' asked Galderon politely, unsure if he wanted to know.

'After the events in Valastry, Zelavaine and I were being hunted. We managed to escape Valastry and find sanctuary in the Spellbound Woods. For a time, we tried to live in isolation and peace, hidden from the world and the past.

But I could not look at or feel for Zelavaine the same way after what she did that day, and for years, she became angrier and angrier and loathed the world and everyone in it. She wanted revenge on the royal families by offering them terrible curses, cloaked as spectacular gifts.'

The King and Queen both shared a fearful glance at

each other, dreading what they were about to be told.

'It was then she malevolently offered your grandmother, Queen Thipthania, the Lake of Wishes and the knowledge of how one could make a Golden Wish, granted once in a lifetime to each of the Royal Family members.

Zelavaine knew that this gift would be far too grand to be ignored, and so it led to the first Golden Wish that was made, which in turn caused the death of the Queen, Thipthania.'

'You were partied to this curse? The murder of my ancestor!' the King exploded with rage as Vanadae, Galderon and Queen Katarina watched in horror.

'No, my lord King. I had separated from her, but when I was told of this so-called Golden Wish during my exile, I knew immediately that it was of her making. I went in search of her to hold her accountable…' said Elzagron in torment.

'It was then that we fought each other viciously in the Spellbound Woods. My powers were no match for hers, and I almost lost my life. Zelavaine thought me dead and left me in the caverns of the now-called Flying Waterfall.

After a time, I was able to move, and in despair and hatred, I went into hiding, serving the Royal House of

Theos as the King and Queen's advisor and Sage. This was the only way I could repent for the terrible actions of Zelavaine.

What she has been doing these past decades I cannot say, but now she will be aware of my existence and will prepare for more hateful acts. We must take action.'

'We will, Elzagron,' King Magnus the Mighty began. 'But not this day. After hearing these scandalous revelations, I fear I am in dire need of the strongest drink in all Splendania!

Come, I need rest and we'll all freeze before long, back to the Palace.'

The King gestured towards the Palace, smiling at his family, putting on a strong face.

'Father, you must allow me to accompany you and Elzagron on this Witch Hunt,' Vanadae requested sternly. 'I also make it my task to escort the Golden Unicorn back to the Spellbound Woods to find her family; I know where to take her. This so-called Zelavaine will be made to answer for her crimes against our family!'

King Magnus and Queen Katarina exchanged a glance of understanding as this would mark the beginning of Vanadae's destiny.

'Where will you take her, my daughter?' asked Queen Katarina; it was a question she already knew the answer to.

'The Cave of Eternity,' replied Vanadae with absolute certainty. 'Though this time we venture through the Spellbound Woods, I will need a weapon. I am sure Father has one or two to spare?' Vanadae asked, flashing a cheeky grin at King Magnus the Mighty's proud face.

'I'm sure I can find something perfect for you in the depths of my armoury, my beautiful daughter,' said King Magnus the Mighty, now overwhelmed with pride and happiness that Vanadae finally showed interest in his weapons.

At this, Galderon looked down at the spectacular sword, Starbolt, attached to his belt and wondered inwardly what more he could accomplish with this power.

In light of the newly hatched plans of Vanadae and Elzagron, Galderon knew he must begin training for a journey he thought would never come.

He was now sure of his path; to travel to Ovamthia, leading the Frozen Hunt, and to be the first Splendanian to ever face down and slay an Ice Dragon atop the cliffs of Dagger Falls. He knew that with training and with Starbolt, this would one day soon be fulfilled.

Galderon did not mention this as he was still in a great amount of relief and wonder at the events that had just unfolded before him. He was overjoyed to see his father be brought back to life, but also in trepidation as to watching his father die before him, cursed by the Golden Wish.

Magic was now clearly something that still existed, and Elzagron had proven it could be wielded. Thoughts of wonder came flooding into Galderon's mind about his enchanting sword and the potential for power that he could maybe wield himself.

King Magnus the Mighty led the way back to the Palace of Theos with the help of Vanadae and Elzagron, as more and more stars flickered brightly in the night's sky.

Queen Katarina the Paladin and Galderon followed in silence, contemplating what had just happened. The Queen was suspiciously quieter than usual, for she was pondering the events that had happened, and what would come to pass in light of this newfound power of Galderon, and Elzagron being revealed as the Long-Lost Wizard of the Woods.

When the Royal Family reached the Palace courtyard before the enormous doorway leading into the warmth, the Palace staff were shocked to see who they thought looked vaguely like Rammir the Cunning, but in a different form.

The King was immediately surrounded by Palace staff and healers as they saw he was weak and being held up by Vanadae. They ushered him to his bed chambers to rest.

'Wine first!' shouted King Magnus the Mighty. 'If you knew what we have all just endured, you would be the first to find solace at the bottom of a bottle! Bring me the 2nd Age Elderberry wine. Might as well make use of it given the circumstances!'

Elderberry wine was the King's favourite drink — a recipe handed down from father to son. Every year, there was a huge elderberry gathering party.

Hundreds of gallons were brewed each year to keep the Royal Wine Cellar stocked to the brim. The Palace staff hunted down this special wine and served the King whilst he sat heavily on his throne.

Elzagron and Queen Katarina joined him in an unknown number of drinks that night, as they discussed Zelavaine and devised a plan to hunt her down.

Vanadae was now very eager to see her beloved Golden Unicorn. She hoped the healers had done their job well and wondered if she was now able to walk.

Vanadae also felt somewhat guilty for Thimien the Unbreakable and Sir Anselet, as she remembered that she had ordered them to keep guard of the Golden Unicorn all this time without leave.

Galderon went straight to bed after returning to the

majestic Palace, his mind filled with thoughts of his future and dreams of accomplishing wonders.

~ CHAPTER 8 ~

THE GOLDEN ONE

Vanadae, wrapped in an elegant green robe, the soft evening breeze flickering her long brown hair, left the Palace and walked quickly and excitedly through the courtyard and down to the Royal Stables.

As Vanadae got closer, she could see glimmers of golden light dancing off the walls, glinting as starlight. To Vanadae's delight, she approached the enchanting golden light of the Unicorn, now standing and eating in her stable. Thimien the Unbreakable and Sir Anselet were still guarding outside the stable gate, weapons in hand.

'Ah, Princess Vanadae!' Sir Anselet said, grinning widely. 'It seems your remarkable creature is on the mend!'

The Golden Unicorn stopped eating and looked at Vanadae in a way that filled her heart with warmth and devotion. There was an understanding between them; it was as though the Golden Unicorn recognised Vanadae and was thankful for protecting her in the Spellbound Woods.

Bewitched by the Golden Unicorn, Vanadae approached in silence, her heart beating faster and faster.

Vanadae thanked the Knights and bid them good night, for she would look after the Golden Unicorn from here onwards. Thimien and Anselet thanked Vanadae for the rare opportunity and gladly took their leave.

Vanadae was now alone with the Golden Unicorn. Mesmerised by her beauty, she held out her hand, inches from the Unicorn's head and closed her eyes.

Vanadae suddenly felt the warmth of the Unicorn on her palm. With a gasp of joy, she looked deeply into the Unicorn's perfect eyes and said, 'All I have ever wanted is to lay eyes on something more beautiful than life itself, and here I am, gazing upon what can only be described as a dream come true. On this day, I name you Aurelia, the Golden One. And I will always protect you.'

Vanadae, completely entranced by Aurelia, unlocked the stable gate and led her out into the Royal

Gardens of Theos.

Her way was lit by the stunning golden light emitting from Aurelia, as the moon reflected off her shimmering coat. Aurelia's leg had healed fast, and she was able to trot and play with Vanadae, seemingly dancing together in the gardens in joyous frivolity.

The King, Queen and Elzagron were still drinking and discussing theories and plans when they were politely interrupted by their head staff member, Bamfry.

'My apologies for the interruption, your majesty. There is something you may well want to see. Come to the window.'

The King stood and found himself immediately sitting again. It was then he realised the wine was stronger than anticipated, even for one as large as him!

With a small laugh, Queen Katarina helped him to the window as gracefully as she could. To their astonishment, they saw the golden light of Aurelia illuminating the endless flowers of their garden, whilst innocently and joyfully spinning and trotting around Vanadae, who, unaware of her onlookers, was in utter bliss, laughing sweetly as she danced around Aurelia as if to music playing from their hearts.

This beautiful and unforgettable sight brought elation to the King, and he embraced Queen Katarina with an affectionate hug as they watched together. Elzagron smiled and was filled with hope, as he left the King and Queen looking out in peace.

Vanadae wrapped her arms around Aurelia's neck and held her tightly; there was a connection between them that seemed as if it could never be broken.

She led Aurelia back to the stables, and when she turned around, she was startled by King Magnus the Mighty and an entourage of Knights including Thimien the Unbreakable and Anselet.

'Father, what are you doing here so late?' Vanadae asked, trying to catch her breath.

'I could ask you the same question, but I already know,' the King replied, smiling, as he looked upon the dazzling light of Aurelia. 'Have you given this majestic creature a name, my daughter?' the King asked.

'Aurelia, the Golden One,' Vanadae replied and gleamed from ear to ear whilst looking at her in affection.

'Aurelia, your blinding grace and beauty are more than enough to simply look upon once in a lifetime than to take as a foolish and selfish trophy.

There are no words I can say that will make amends for my actions, but it is my royal decree that you go free and unharmed from this day forth.'

The Knights surrounding the King shared a hopeful look as they had become fond of Aurelia whilst guarding her, and they could see the love Vanadae shared with her.

'We will return you to your family and protect you and your kind forevermore.'

Vanadae ran to King Magnus, took him in her arms and whispered, 'Thank you, Father. I love you.'

When Vanadae reached the comfort of her exceptionally large and beautifully decorated bedroom, she had a wonderful sense of home. She took a moment to look around in appreciation, for the Royal Golden Hunt had taken its toll and it was time to rest.

Vanadae's room was filled with ornate furniture and purple draping's adorned with dragons, and unicorns sewed into the material with golden thread covering the huge doorway to her very own balcony.

Vanadae suddenly remembered her magnificently mystical Pixie Pebble in her satchel and found the perfect place to display it — atop her fireplace.

Knowing that one Pixie Pebble was just the start of a quest to find the Lost City of Pixies, she vowed whilst placing her hand firmly upon the smooth and bright Pixie Pebble that she would find the other two and finally be the one to find this hidden city. Vanadae's bed called to her, and she slept almost immediately, filled with dreams of adventure, wonder and hope.

~ CHAPTER 9 ~

OF WITCHES & DRAGONS

The next morning, Vanadae was awoken by King Magnus the Mighty, who was knocking on her door excitedly.

'Vanadae, wake up!' King Magnus shouted. 'We have weapons to choose from and plans to be settled. Make your way down to the table for breakfast at once! There is much to be done, and much to be eaten, if Galderon has left any, that is!'

Vanadae gleamed with a beautiful smile and got dressed for breakfast. Before anything else, Vanadae wanted to ensure Aurelia was safely in her stable and healed.

Thus, Vanadae quickly made her way to the Royal

Stables and found a large crowd around Aurelia's stable, all of them muttering inquisitively, in awe of her.

As Vanadae motioned towards the stable, the crowd dispersed and made way for her to proceed.

'Your Grace,' the elder stable boy began. 'Magic has been cast on this animal. It must have been.'

'What are you talking about? Is Aurelia, ok?' Vanadae inquired nervously, whilst finally getting close enough to see the overwhelming beauty of Aurelia.

'Her leg, my Princess, there is no sign of any damage at all. She has been fully healed!' said the stable boy excitedly.

Vanadae smiled and chuckled in glee whilst thinking that it must have been Elzagron who had magically healed her. Vanadae stroked Aurelia's wondrous golden coat and put her hand on her head, between Aurelia's eyes, with affection, remembering what a phenomenal night they shared, dancing in the moonlight.

'Make sure Aurelia is well fed and kept safe, I will return shortly!' said Vanadae to the stable boys, as she swiftly returned to the Palace.

Galderon, as usual, was already where the food was and helping himself to his second plate of wild boar sausages and eggs.

He sat next to Queen Katarina the Paladin, who was watching him eat in astonishment as to where all the food he would usually eat goes.

The Prince was in an energetic mood today and could sense the excitement in the air concerning weapons and witches.

Unbeknownst to his family, this was also the day when Galderon would make an announcement that would set him on his way to becoming what he had always wanted to be — a celebrated monster hunter with his very own Special, just like his father and his favourite Knights.

As Vanadae greeted Galderon and Queen Katarina good morning and the Palace staff served her breakfast, she was in high spirits. She wondered about the kind of weapon that would suit her best and then decided to ask her expert brother for his opinion.

'So, Mr future Monster Slayer,' Vanadae said cheerily, half-mocking her brother. 'What do you think would be a fitting weapon for me? You have spent half your days in that armoury, there must be something.'

Just as Galderon was about to give his opinion, King Magnus the Mighty burst through the door, followed by Elzagron, who was looking apprehensive and nervous until his eyes met Vanadae's, and they shared a smile of understanding and love.

This smile was the confirmation Vanadae needed for her suspicions, that indeed, he had used his magic to heal Aurelia's leg; there were no words needed to be said by either of them.

King Magnus was carrying a jumbled collection of swords, axes, daggers, and shields. Galderon thought he dropped them rather dangerously, in an untidy heap on the dining room floor with enthusiasm. It was too early for such a great amount of noise, Queen Katarina thought.

Galderon smiled along with Vanadae at the sight of their father so happy and excitable. He began to pick different weapons up and wave them around, whilst explaining in great detail, how to use them; they all found him amusing to watch. It was as if the King was battling the very air around him.

'That shield, Father, it is so beautiful and looks very light! May I try it for size?' Vanadae asked with her eyes fixed on a small and shining shield, adorned with a beautifully embossed Griffin's head protruding from the centre of the metal and red jewels surrounding its edge.

'A shield?' King Magnus asked in surprise. 'Interesting choice, but I suppose a shield would be handy against a Witch if all else fails. Here, its name is apparently "Griffinsbane," or so Elzagron told me years ago.'

A nod and a smile from Elzagron confirmed the name. 'Try it by all means!'

As Vanadae picked up the handsome shield, she instantly knew it was the right choice; so light and manoeuvrable, and not to mention, the astounding beauty of its design.

The sight of Vanadae wielding one of King Magnus's treasures was truly a sight to behold, and the King was overjoyed to see her this way.

'You will need a sword too!' Galderon said, whilst picking out a longsword far too big and heavy for Vanadae — or so Queen Katarina thought. And she was right, as Vanadae struggled to hold the sword.

'No, no, no,' Queen Katarina said in humorous frustration. 'This is no weapon for a Princess of Theos. Here, this is a much better fit.'

Queen Katarina gave Vanadae a fascinating dagger in a sheath of gold and lined with emeralds. Vanadae smiled at the sight of this weapon, far much more to her liking than a brutish longsword.

As Vanadae pulled the blade from its sheath, she instantly felt it was perfect for her — an elegantly-smithed blade of silver as sharp as a razor, and small enough to conceal.

King Magnus the Mighty found the matching belt and attached the dagger to Vanadae's waist.

'There!' King Magnus beamed, whilst taking in the

sight of Vanadae with Griffinsbane in her left hand and her beautiful dagger properly attached. 'A true warrior of Splendania. I couldn't be prouder. Quickly now, let us finish breakfast and prepare for a Witch Hunt.'

Elzagron was impressed with this vision of Vanadae, and as he studied her new look, he thought inwardly that perhaps she was indeed the key to the end of the Witch, whatever form that would take.

He then began to explain that this Witch Hunt must be one of great stealth and only a small party of them would go back into the Spellbound Woods; himself, Vanadae, King Magnus, Thimien the Unbreakable and Sir Anselet.

After hearing this, Galderon gave Queen Katarina a tentative look, which meant he was about to speak.

'Mother? Father?' Galderon called out hesitantly. 'If I am not to join you on this mission, I know what I must do. I will require training with master Swordswoman, Amelina the Agile.

Now I know the path I must take to distant lands and never accomplished feats.'

Galderon pulled out a drawing of Ovamthia and an Ice Dragon, then stuck a dagger in the dragon with great purpose.

As soon as Galderon stuck the dagger in the Ice

Dragon drawing, the whole family and Elzagron looked at Galderon with both intrigue and concern. Then, suddenly, there was a stern knock on the dining room door. Everyone cast their eyes from the dagger towards the large, opulently crafted door, opened by Bamfry.

'Ah, it seems your punctuality, as always, knows no equal, Lady Amelina,' said Bamfry with a warm smile and a gesture for her to enter the room. Amelina had a profound and mystical way of always turning up when someone mentioned they needed her services.

King Magnus and Queen Katarina looked at Amelina with brief scepticism and then welcomed her to their Royal table to be seated. Amelina the Agile was a beautiful woman of Valastry, with long, plaited blonde hair and large green eyes.

She had the air of someone who had lived an extraordinarily adventurous life. Amelina's ability with swords was legendary across Splendania, and so, King Magnus the Mighty had employed her services to train his Kingsmen to be unstoppable.

Galderon was temporarily awestruck and could not seem to muster any words in her presence just yet; Vanadae found his silence most amusing.

'So, it is true, Prince Galderon,' said Amelina with intrigue, in a Valastrian accent. 'You have acquired the fabled sword, Starbolt, and have used its power?' Amelina added in absolute fascination.

Finally finding the courage to respond after what seemed to Vanadae like an embarrassing amount of time, Galderon was ready to speak to Amelina.

'Something resonates within it; a power I was able to wield when in the Spellbound Woods, defending the Unicorn and Vanadae. And I will use it to be the first Splendanian to kill an Ice Dragon atop Dagger Falls,' said Galderon, looking rather proud of himself.

King Magnus looked at Queen Katarina with regret, as this was a sombre reminder of everything that had happened.

'Well now,' Amelina began, stunned by Galderon's determination. 'I am sure you are eager to know what else this sword can do, and how to use it to accomplish this task. I can help you there. Come, let us begin.'

Galderon looked at Queen Katarina, in a bid to seek her approval. Once she nodded encouragingly, Amelina led Galderon out of the dining room to begin his first training session.

Vanadae was now beginning to feel anxious about the looming hunt for Zelavaine. She knew that she would be well protected, but after hearing what Zelavaine was capable of, and how she enchanted King Magnus, it filled her heart with fear and doubt.

Despite these feelings, Vanadae knew that she must find her courage and resolve, for the Witch had to be stopped, once and for all. Now aware of Elzagron's deception and power, there was no knowing what evil Zelavaine would be planning.

'Fear not, my princess,' Elzagron said reassuringly, upon noticing the anxious look on Vanadae's face. 'I will keep you from harm and fear in the Woods. Together, we must put an end to Zelavaine's curses. All she has done can never be forgiven.'

'Perhaps there is another way to stop her? If we can spare a life, we must do so. I want revenge upon her, but I do not want to become a killer, Elzagron.'

King Magnus and Queen Katarina heard this, and both were overjoyed that their daughter felt this way, even though they all had reasonable cause to kill Zelavaine.

Capturing her alive was more important, to learn about what she had been doing and for her to answer for her crimes from the rulers of each realm.

King Magnus kissed Queen Katarina on the cheek and left the dining room to find Thimien the Unbreakable and Sir Anselet to prepare for the next adventure — The Last Witch Hunt.

'Come with me, Vanadae,' Queen Katarina said. 'I have something for you in the Royal Library. You will find it most useful and comforting on your travels I think.'

Excited as to what this could be, Vanadae put her shield, Griffinsbane, on the table and followed her mother to the Royal Library, whilst Elzagron went to the Lake of Wishes to meditate in isolation.

There was much he needed to think about. He also needed to plan for the possible dangers they would face when they find Zelavaine.

When Queen Katarina entered the Royal Library, she picked a book from a locked drawer and put it on the vast table in the centre of the room.

'Here, you will need this,' said Queen Katarina as she gestured to the magnificent book with the words, "The Compendium of Hidden Places and Creatures. The Accounts of Vilso Ark."

Vanadae was in awe of this book, it looked so inviting to read, and she was certain it would lead her to phenomenal places of old, where she dreamed of exploring and witnessing the majestic creatures all across Splendania.

'Mother, who is Vilso Ark?' asked Vanadae, staring at the book's cover.

'He was a great explorer of the 2nd Age; he was responsible for most of the knowledge about the magical creatures, monsters and hidden places of the three realms.

This book contains information that I hope you will find useful and entertaining. I can see that it is your destiny to add to this book or to write your own, based on your very own account.

There are so many wonders out there, Vanadae, even lands beyond Splendania! There are details about a distant Kingdom, named Pharia, that is surrounded by water and all manner of enormous beasts that dwell within its depths.'

Queen Katarina put her hands on Vanadae's shoulders, looked lovingly into her dazzling eyes and continued with all seriousness, 'It is you that holds the key to turning Splendania around. For too long, we have rewarded the killing of innocent creatures. I have hidden this book from your father, for obvious reasons. It is now your responsibility to uncover the mysteries of Splendania.'

'I will, Mother. I will explore every corner of these realms and protect the creatures forevermore,' replied Vanadae as she opened the spellbinding book and began to read enthusiastically.

Vanadae had never heard of other Kingdoms, and this excited her beyond anything. Ovamthia and Valastry were already within her reach. *What other wonders will I find in Pharia?* she wondered.

'Take it back to your room and pack, my dear. Your

father and Elzagron will be eager to begin the Last Witch Hunt. You must promise me to stay by your father's side, and if you have the power to save a life, you must.'

'I promise,' Vanadae replied solemnly, with her hand on her heart.

EPILOGUE

As the sun rose over the peaks of the mountains at the far side of the Lake of Wishes, there was only the faint sound of gentle waves splashing upon the shores.

Elzagron was kneeling with his eyes shut, in pure concentration as he meditated on the events that had happened, the cost of using his magic to return King Magnus the Mighty back from the dead and reversing the Golden Wish.

His mind became troubled and dark, and then suddenly, from the quiet of the shores, he heard loud whirring and unnerving whispering inside his head, causing Elzagron to remain entirely motionless against his will, shaking to escape this magical grasp.

'Returned from the dead, my love?' a hoarse, unnervingly familiar voice from within Elzagron's mind said from nowhere, filling him with the unrelenting dread that he could not help but remember.

A faded vision of Zelavaine appeared, shrouded in fog. An old, hideously ugly woman with threatening baggy eyes of yellow was cowering over her Seeing Crystals, trembling weakly and in desperation, as she spoke cruelly to Elzagron.

'My grip upon you is stronger now than ever before, you, weak old fool. You will bring me the King, Vanadae and the Golden Unicorn that is rightfully mine.

They will pay for their theft. I need it back; after all, it was always mine to use. I will finally destroy the despot, King Magnus, and his beloved, vexatious and meddling daughter, once and for all. You have done well in earning their trust by undoing the Golden Wish.

Now, it is time to finish this together. There is much to do. Lead them to me.'

With a heavy heart, filled with unshakable fear, knowing that he could never escape Zelavaine's control and the wrath she was preparing to bring down upon Vanadae and King Magnus, Elzagron replied meekly, 'I am yours to command as always, my love.'

The harrowing vision of Zelavaine ended, and far

away, deep within the Spellbound Woods, thick mist and shadow swirled around the Enchanted Rocks of Elianth, as a cruel smile curled upon Zelavaine's grotesque and unforgiving face.

'I will bring about the end of their beloved King, and they will all see how wicked I can be.'

THE END

About The Author

Born and raised on a beautiful farm overlooking the Black Mountains and the Brecon Beacons on the border of Wales and England, T.O. Griffiths grew up fascinated by animals, sharks most of all. He was lucky enough to be surrounded by farm animals - including the magnificent peacocks - and a stunning view. As a boy, he used to write short stories and poems, somewhat inspired by Alice in Wonderland.

With a large collection of swords, axes and armour himself, his fascination with weaponry has helped inspire certain characters T.O. Griffiths has created in Splendania.

With a busy job and life moving forward, time to focus and complete the book became a labour of love for T.O. Griffiths, but something he was determined to accomplish.

The story coming into existence was completely spontaneous; he was asked to make up a bedtime story for his girlfriend to help her sleep. It was not helpful, however, as he was then up all night, writing it down instead of finishing the story for her, until now.

Tales of Splendania had been rattling around T.O. Griffiths' head for many years and the story evolved and swayed this way and that, and now, he is extremely excited to share it with you and hopes you enjoy it as much as he has enjoyed creating the World of Splendania.

The story continues in Tales of Splendania: A Heart of Ice, which takes Vanadae and Galderon on more whirlwind adventures throughout Splendania and beyond!

TALES OF SPLENDANIA

A HEART OF ICE

T.O. GRIFFITHS

Acknowledgements

Thank you so much to everyone who has supported me on my writing adventure. I sincerely hope you enjoyed the World of Splendania that I have created.

A special thank you to Gem. Without your gift of the notebook inscribed; 'The Future is Bright,' that accompanied me during far too many late nights, most of the ideas and story arcs would not exist as I would have forgotten everything!

A big thank you to fellow author, Rosie Wylor-Owen, who has been an incredible help to me throughout my journey.

Thank you all.

Printed in Great Britain
by Amazon